BROWN'S
RULE OF THE ROAD MANUAL

BROWN'S
RULE OF THE ROAD MANUAL

BROWN'S
Rule of the Road Manual

THE RULE OF THE ROAD AT SEA
Illustrated by Coloured Diagrams

REVISED BY

H. H. BROWN, D.S.C.,* R.D., F.R.A.S.

EXTRA MASTER

GLASGOW

BROWN, SON & FERGUSON, LTD., NAUTICAL PUBLISHERS

52 DARNLEY STREET

First Edition – 1928
Seventeenth Edition 1981

ISBN 0 85174 405 2
ISBN 0 85174 254 8 (16th edition)

© 1981 BROWN, SON & FERGUSON, LTD., GLASGOW, G41 2SG
Printed and made in Great Britain

PREFACE

THE Rule of the Road at Sea is of paramount importance to those who assume control of a vessel as upon its practical application depends in a large measure the Safety of life and property.

The requisite knowledge can only be acquired by careful study and observation and the object of the book is to provide a means to this end. In this connection *Brown's Rule of the Road Manual* has for many years served as a guide to the Examinations for the various grades of Certificates of Competency conducted by the Department of Trade. It is specially suitable for study at sea, the sequence of matter being arranged for that purpose, and the diagrams, questions and answers will be found most helpful and informative. This book, while retaining the form of previous editions which proved to be highly popular, has been revised to meet the requiremenis of the International Regulations for Preventing Collisions at Sea, 1972, which come into force on 1st January, 1976, and The Maritime Buoyage System 'A', in force N.W. Europe, 1980.

CONTENTS

CONTENTS

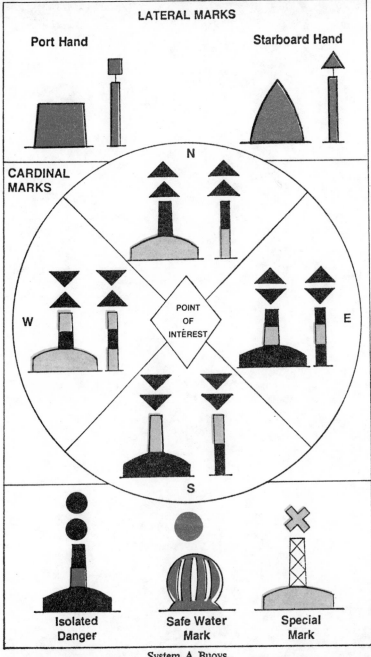

System A Buoys.

UNIFORM SYSTEM OF MARITIME BUOYAGE

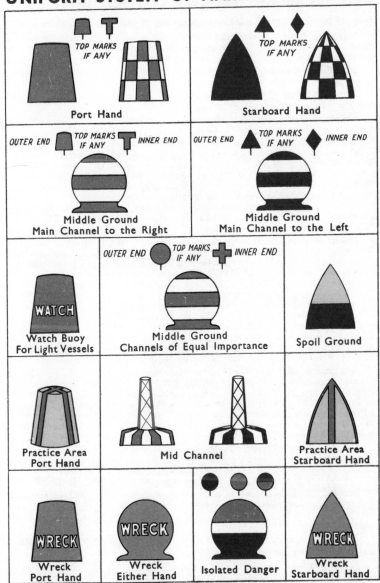

TOP MARKS IF ANY

Port Hand

TOP MARKS IF ANY

Starboard Hand

OUTER END — TOP MARKS IF ANY — INNER END

Middle Ground
Main Channel to the Right

OUTER END — TOP MARKS IF ANY — INNER END

Middle Ground
Main Channel to the Left

WATCH

Watch Buoy
For Light Vessels

OUTER END — TOP MARKS IF ANY — INNER END

Middle Ground
Channels of Equal Importance

Spoil Ground

Practice Area
Port Hand

Mid Channel

Practice Area
Starboard Hand

WRECK

Wreck
Port Hand

WRECK

Wreck
Either Hand

Isolated Danger

WRECK

Wreck
Starboard Hand

BROWN, SON & FERGUSON, Ltd., Glasgow G41 2SG   Copyright   Printed and made in Great Britain

UNIFORM SYSTEM OF MARITIME BUOYAGE

Adopted by the General Lighthouse Authorities of the United Kingdom (1947)

Starboard Hand.—Means that side of the channel which will be on the right hand of the Mariner when going with the main stream of flood tide, or when entering a harbour, river or estuary from seaward.

Port Hand.—Means that side which will be on the left hand of the Mariner in the same circumstances.

Principal Types of Marks.—The Principal types of marks employed are: Conical, can and spherical.

Shapes of Topmarks.—The topmarks for which provision is made are: Cone, can, sphere, diamond, St. George's Cross, "T"

Marking Sides of Channels.—*Starboard-hand marks*—Shape: Conical. Colour: Black, or, for purposes of differentiation, black and white chequers, Topmark (if any): Black cone, point upwards, or, for purposes of differentiation, a black diamond, except at the entrance to a channel. Light (if any): White showing 1 or 3 flashes. *Port-hand marks*—Shape: Can, Colour: Red, or, for purposes of differentiation, red and white chequers. Topmark (if any): Red can, or, for purposes of differentiation, a red "T", except at the entrance to a channel. Light (if any): Red showing any number of flashes up to 4, or white showing 2 or 4 flashes.

Middle Ground Marks.—Marks at the ends of middle grounds have the following characteristics. Shape: Spherical. Colour: R.W.H.B. (red and white horizontal bands) where the main channel is to the *right* or the channels are of *equal* importance. B.W.H.B. (black and white horizontal bands) where the main channel is to the *left*. Topmarks (if any): (a) Main channel to the *right*. Outer end, a can painted Red, Inner end, a "T" painted Red. (b) Main channel to the *left*. Outer end, a cone painted Black, Inner end, a diamond painted Black. (c) Channels of *equal* importance. Outer end, a sphere painted Red, Inner end, a St. George's Cross painted Red. Light (if any): As far as possible lights will be distinctive, but no colours will be used other than white or red and neither colour nor rhythm will be such as to lead to uncertainty as to side on which the mark shall be passed.

Mid Channel Marks.—Mid-channel marks serve to indicate the deep water channel or fairway. Shape: To be distinctive and different from the principal characteristic shapes (viz. conical, can and spherical). Colour: B.W.V.S. or R.W.V.S. (black and white or red and white vertical stripes). Topmark (if any): To be a distinctive shape other than cone, can or sphere. Light (if any): To be of a character different from neighbouring lights on marks at the sides of the channel.

Isolated Danger Marks.—Shape: Spherical Colour: Wide black and red horizontal bands separated by a narrow white band. Topmark (if any): Sphere painted black or red, or half black and half red, horizontally. Light (if any): White or red with flashing character.

Landfall Marks.—Shape: In accordance with rules for channel marking. Colour: Black and White or Red and White vertical stripes, Light (if any) Flashing character.

NOTE—

Mid Channel Marks.—The usual shape is the pillar buoy and topmarks, if any, may include the double cross $\left(\begin{smallmatrix} + \\ + \end{smallmatrix}\right)$.

Landfall Marks.—Usually pillar buoys and the topmarks, if any, may include the St. Andrews Cross ($\times$).

International Regulations
for
Preventing Collisions
at Sea

GLASGOW
BROWN, SON & FERGUSON, LIMITED
4-10 DARNLEY STREET

New Edition – June 1983
Reprinted – 1986

ISBN 0 85174 463 X

© 1986 BROWN, SON & FERGUSON, LTD., GLASGOW G41 2SD
Made and Printed in Great Britain

INTERNATIONAL REGULATIONS

FOR

PREVENTING COLLISIONS AT SEA, 1983

PART A. GENERAL

RULE 1

Application

(*a*) These Rules shall apply to all vessels upon the high seas and in all waters connected therewith navigable by seagoing vessels.

(*b*) Nothing in these Rules shall interfere with the operation of special rules made by an appropriate authority for roadsteads, harbours, rivers, lakes or inland waterways connected with the high seas and navigable by seagoing vessels. Such special rules shall conform as closely as possible to these Rules.

(*c*) Nothing in these Rules shall interfere with the operation of any special rules made by the Government of any State with respect to additional station or signal lights, shapes or whistle signals for ships of war and vessels proceeding under convoy, or with respect to additional station or signal lights or shapes for fishing vessels engaged in fishing as a fleet. These additional station or signal lights, shapes or whistle signals shall, so far as possible, be such that they cannot be mistaken for any light, shape or signal authorized elsewhere under these Rules.

(*d*) Traffic separation schemes may be adopted by the Organization for the purpose of these Rules.

(*e*) Whenever the Government concerned shall have determined that a vessel of special construction or purpose cannot comply fully with the provisions of any of these Rules with respect to the number, position, range or arc of visibility of lights or shapes, as well as to the disposition and characteristics of sound-signalling appliances, without interfering with the special function of the vessel, such vessel shall comply with such other provisions in regard to the number, position, range or arc of visibility of lights or shapes, as well as to the disposition and characteristics of sound-signalling appliances, as her Government shall have determined to be the closest possible compliance with these Rules in respect to that vessel.

Rule 2

Responsibility

(*a*) Nothing in these Rules shall exonerate any vessel, or the owner, master or crew thereof, from the consequences of any neglect to comply with these Rules or of the neglect of any precaution which may be required by the ordinary practice of seamen, or by the special circumstances of the case.

(*b*) In construing and complying with these Rules due regard shall be had to all dangers of navigation and collision and to any special circumstances, including the limitations of the vessels involved, which may make a departure from these Rules necessary to avoid immediate danger.

Rule 3

General definitions

For the purpose of these Rules, except where the context otherwise requires:

(*a*) The word " vessel " includes every description of water craft, including non-displacement craft and seaplanes, used or capable of being used as a means of transportation on water.

(*b*) The term " power-driven vessel " means any vessel propelled by machinery.

(*c*) The term " sailing vessel " means any vessel under sail provided that propelling machinery, if fitted, is not being used.

(*d*) The term " vessel engaged in fishing " means any vessel fishing with nets, lines, trawls or other fishing apparatus which restrict manoeuvrability, but does not include a vessel fishing with trolling lines or other fishing apparatus which do not restrict manoeuvrability.

(*e*) The word " seaplane " includes any aircraft designed to manoeuvre on the water.

(*f*) The term " vessel not under command " means a vessel which through some exceptional circumstance is unable to manoeuvre as required by these Rules and is therefore unable to keep out of the way of another vessel.

(*g*) The term " vessel restricted in her ability to manoeuvre " means a vessel which from the nature of her work is restricted in her ability to manoeuvre as required by these Rules and is therefore unable to keep out of the way of another vessel.

The term 'vessels restricted in their ability to manoeuvre' shall include but not be limited to:

(i) a vessel engaged in laying, servicing or picking up a navigation mark, submarine cable or pipeline;

(ii) a vessel engaged in dredging, surveying or underwater operations;

    (iii) a vessel engaged in replenishment or transferring persons, provisions or cargo while underway;

    (iv) a vessel engaged in the launching or recovery of aircraft;

    (v) a vessel engaged in mineclearance operations;

    (vi) a vessel engaged in a towing operation such as severely restricts the towing vessel and her tow in their ability to deviate from their course.

(h) The term " vessel constrained by her draught " means a power-driven vessel which because of her draught in relation to the available depth of water is severely restricted in her ability to deviate from the course she is following.

(i) The word " underway " means that a vessel is not at anchor, or made fast to the shore, or aground.

(j) The words " length " and " breadth " of a vessel mean her length overall and greatest breadth.

(k) Vessels shall be deemed to be in sight of one another only when one can be observed visually from the other.

(l) The term " restricted visibility " means any condition in which visibility is restricted by fog, mist, falling snow, heavy rainstorms, sandstorms or any other similar causes.

PART B. STEERING AND SAILING RULES

Section I. Conduct of vessels in any condition of visibility

RULE 4

Application

Rules in this Section apply in any condition of visibility.

RULE 5

Look-out

Every vessel shall at all times maintain a proper look-out by sight and hearing as well as by all available means appropriate in the prevailing circumstances and conditions so as to make a full appraisal of the situation and of the risk of collision.

Rule 6

Safe speed

Every vessel shall at all times proceed at a safe speed so that she can take proper and effective action to avoid collision and be stopped within a distance appropriate to the prevailing circumstances and conditions.

In determining a safe speed the following factors shall be among those taken into account:

(*a*) **By all vessels:**

(i) the state of visibility;

(ii) the traffic density including concentrations of fishing vessels or any other vessels;

(iii) the manoeuvrability of the vessel with special reference to stopping distance and turning ability in the prevailing conditions;

(iv) at night the presence of background light such as from shore lights or from back scatter of her own lights;

(v) the state of wind, sea and current, and the proximity of navigational hazards;

(vi) the draught in relation to the available depth of water.

(*b*) Additionally, by vessels with operational radar:

(i) the characteristics, efficiency and limitations of the radar equipment;

(ii) any constraints imposed by the radar range scale in use;

(iii) the effect on radar detection of the sea state, weather and other sources of interference;

(iv) the possibility that small vessels, ice and other floating objects may not be detected by radar at an adequate range;

(v) the number, location and movement of vessels detected by radar;

(vi) the more exact assessment of the visibility that may be possible when radar is used to determine the range of vessels or other objects in the vicinity.

Rule 7

Risk of collision

(*a*) Every vessel shall use all available means appropriate to the prevailing circumstances and conditions to determine if risk of collision exists. If there is any doubt such risk shall be deemed to exist.

(*b*) Proper use shall be made of radar equipment if fitted and operational, including long-range scanning to obtain early warning of risk of collision and radar plotting or equivalent systematic observation of detected objects.

(*c*) Assumptions shall not be made on the basis of scanty information, especially scanty radar information.

(*d*) In determining if risk of collision exists the following considerations shall be among those taken into account:

    (i) such risk shall be deemed to exist if the compass bearing of an approaching vessel does not appreciably change.

    (ii) such risk may sometimes exist even when an appreciable bearing change is evident, particularly when approaching a very large vessel or a tow or when approaching a vessel at close range.

RULE 8

Action to avoid collision

(*a*) Any action taken to avoid collision shall, if the circumstances of the case admit, be positive, made in ample time and with due regard to the observance of good seamanship.

(*b*) Any alteration of course and/or speed to avoid collision shall, if the circumstances of the case admit, be large enough to be readily apparent to another vessel observing visually or by radar; a succession of small alterations of course and/or speed should be avoided.

(*c*) If there is sufficient sea room, alteration of course alone may be the most effective action to avoid a close-quarters situation provided that it is made in good time, is substantial and does not result in another close-quarters situation.

(*d*) Action taken to avoid collision with another vessel shall be such as to result in passing at a safe distance. The effectiveness of the action shall be carefully checked until the other vessel is finally past and clear.

(*e*) If necessary to avoid collision or allow more time to assess the situation, a vessel shall slacken her speed or take all way off by stopping or reversing her means of propulsion.

RULE 9

Narrow channels

(*a*) A vessel proceeding along the course of a narrow channel or fairway shall keep as near to the outer limit of the channel or fairway which lies on her starboard side as is safe and practicable.

(*b*) A vessel of less than 20 metres in length or a sailing vessel shall not impede the passage of a vessel which can safely navigate only within a narrow channel or fairway.

(*c*) A vessel engaged in fishing shall not impede the passage of any other vessel navigating within a narrow channel or fairway.

(*d*) A vessel shall not cross a narrow channel or fairway if such crossing impedes the passage of a vessel which can safely navigate only within such channel or fairway. The latter vessel may use the sound signal prescribed in Rule 34 (*d*) if in doubt as to the intention of the crossing vessel.

(*e*) (i) In a narrow channel or fairway when overtaking can take place only if the vessel to be overtaken has to take action to permit safe passing, the vessel intending to overtake shall indicate her intention by sounding the appropriate signal prescribed in Rule 34 (*c*) (i). The vessel to be overtaken shall, if in agreement, sound the appropriate signal prescribed in Rule 34 (*c*) (ii) and take steps to permit safe passing. If in doubt she may sound the signals prescribed in Rule 34 (*d*).

(ii) This Rule does not relieve the overtaking vessel of her obligation under Rule 13.

(*f*) A vessel nearing a bend or an area of a narrow channel or fairway where other vessels may be obscured by an intervening obstruction shall navigate with particular alertness and caution and shall sound the appropriate signal prescribed in Rule 34 (*e*).

(*g*) Any vessel shall, if the circumstances of the case admit, avoid anchoring in a narrow channel.

RULE 10

Traffic separation schemes

(*a*) This Rule applies to traffic separation schemes adopted by the Organization:

(*b*) A vessel using a traffic separation scheme shall:

(i) proceed in the appropriate traffic lane in the general direction of traffic flow for that lane;

(ii) so far as practicable keep clear of a traffic separation line or separation zone;

(iii) normally join or leave a traffic lane at the termination of the lane, but when joining or leaving from either side shall do so at as small an angle to the general direction of traffic flow as practicable.

(*c*) A vessel shall so far as practicable avoid crossing traffic lanes, but if obliged to do so shall cross as nearly as practicable at right angles to the general direction of traffic flow.

(*d*) Inshore traffic zones shall not normally be used by through traffic which can safely use the appropriate traffic lane within the adjacent traffic separation scheme. However, vessels of less than 20 metres in length and sailing vessels may under all circumstances use inshore traffic zones.

(*e*) A vessel other than a crossing vessel or a vessel joining or leaving a.lane shall not normally enter a separation zone or cross a separation line except:

(i) in cases of emergency to avoid immediate danger;

(ii) to engage in fishing within a separation zone.

(*f*) A vessel navigating in areas near the terminations of traffic separation schemes shall do so with particular caution.

(*g*) A vessel shall so far as practicable avoid anchoring in a traffic separation scheme or in areas near its terminations.

(*h*) A vessel not using a traffic separation scheme shall avoid it by as wide a margin as is practicable.

(*i*) A vessel engaged in fishing shall not impede the passage of any vessel following a traffic lane.

(*j*) A vessel of less than 20 metres in length or a sailing vessel shall not impede the safe passage of a power-driven vessel following a traffic lane.

(*k*) A vessel restricted in her ability to manoeuvre when engaged in an operation for the maintenance of safety of navigation in a traffic separation scheme is exempted from complying with this Rule to the extent necessary to carry out the operation.

(*l*) A vessel restricted in her ability to manoeuvre when engaged in an operation for the laying, servicing or picking up of a submarine cable, within a traffic separation scheme, is exempted from complying with this Rule to the extent necessary to carry out the operation.

Section II. Conduct of vessels in sight of one another

RULE 11
Application
Rules in this Section apply to vessels in sight of one another.

RULE 12
Sailing vessels
(*a*) When two sailing vessels are approaching one another, so as to involve risk of collision, one of them shall keep out of the way of the other as follows:
  (i) when each has the wind on a different side, the vessel which has the wind on the port side shall keep out of the way of the other;
  (ii) when both have the wind on the same side, the vessel which is to windward shall keep out of the way of the vessel which is to leeward;
  (iii) if a vessel with the wind on the port side sees a vessel to windward and cannot determine with certainty whether the other vessel has the wind on the port or on the starboard side, she shall keep out of the way of the other.

(*b*) For the purposes of this Rule the windward side shall be deemed to be the side opposite to that on which the mainsail is carried or, in the case of a square-rigged vessel, the side opposite to that on which the largest fore-and-aft sail is carried.

RULE 13
Overtaking
(*a*) Notwithstanding anything contained in the Rules of Part B, Sections I and II, any vessel overtaking any other shall keep out of the way of the vessel being overtaken.

(b) A vessel shall be deemed to be overtaking when coming up with another vessel from a direction more than 22·5 degrees abaft her beam, that is, in such a position with reference to the vessel she is overtaking, that at night she would be able to see only the sternlight of that vessel but neither of her sidelights.

(c) When a vessel is in doubt as to whether she is overtaking another, she shall assume that this is the case and act accordingly.

(d) Any subsequent alteration of the bearing between the two vessels shall not make the overtaking vessel a crossing vessel within the meaning of these Rules or relieve her of the duty of keeping clear of the overtaken vessel until she is finally past and clear.

RULE 14

Head-on situation

(a) When two power-driven vessels are meeting on reciprocal or nearly reciprocal courses so as to involve risk of collision each shall alter her course to starboard so that each shall pass on the port side of the other.

(b) Such a situation shall be deemed to exist when a vessel sees the other ahead or nearly ahead and by night she could see the masthead lights of the other in a line or nearly in a line and/or both sidelights and by day she observes the corresponding aspect of the other vessel.

(c) When a vessel is in any doubt as to whether such a situation exists she shall assume that it does exist and act accordingly.

RULE 15

Crossing situation

When two power-driven vessels are crossing so as to involve risk of collision, the vessel which has the other on her own starboard side shall keep out of the way and shall, if the circumstances of the case admit, avoid crossing ahead of the other vessel.

RULE 16

Action by give-way vessel

Every vessel which is directed to keep out of the way of another vessel shall, so far as possible, take early and substantial action to keep well clear.

RULE 17

Action by stand-on vessel

(a) (i) Where one of two vessels is to keep out of the way the other shall keep her course and speed.

(ii) The latter vessel may however take action to avoid collision by her manoeuvre alone, as soon as it becomes apparent to her that the vessel required to keep out of the way is not taking appropriate action in compliance with these Rules.

(b) When, from any cause, the vessel required to keep her course and speed finds herself so close that collision cannot be avoided by the action of the give-way vessel alone, she shall take such action as will best aid to avoid collision.

(c) A power-driven vessel which takes action in a crossing situation in accordance with sub-paragraph (a) (ii) of this Rule to avoid collision with another power-driven vessel shall, if the circumstances of the case admit, not alter course to port for a vessel on her own port side.

(d) This Rule does not relieve the give-way vessel of her obligation to keep out of the way.

RULE 18

Responsibilities between vessels

Except where Rules 9, 10 and 13 otherwise require:

(a) A power-driven vessel underway shall keep out of the way of:

  (i) a vessel not under command;

  (ii) a vessel restricted in her ability to manoeuvre;

  (iii) a vessel engaged in fishing;

  (iv) a sailing vessel.

(b) A sailing vessel underway shall keep out of the way of:

  (i) a vessel not under command;

  (ii) a vessel restricted in her ability to manoeuvre;

  (iii) a vessel engaged in fishing.

(c) A vessel engaged in fishing when underway shall, so far as possible, keep out of the way of:

  (i) a vessel not under command;

  (ii) a vessel restricted in her ability to manoeuvre.

(d (i) Any vessel other than a vessel not under command or a vessel restricted in her ability to manoeuvre shall, if the circumstances of the case admit, avoid impeding the safe passage of a vessel constrained by her draught, exhibiting the signals in Rule 28.

  (ii) A vessel constrained by her draught shall navigate with particular caution having full regard to her special condition.

(e) A seaplane on the water shall, in general, keep well clear of all vessels and avoid impeding their navigation. In circumstances, however, where risk of collision exists, she shall comply with the Rules of this Part.

Section III. Conduct of vessels in restricted visibility

RULE 19

Conduct of vessels in restricted visibility

(a) This Rule applies to vessels not in sight of one another when navigating in or near an area of restricted visibility.

(*b*) Every vessel shall proceed at a safe speed adapted to the prevailing circumstances and conditions of restricted visibility. A power-driven vessel shall have her engines ready for immediate manoeuvre.

(*c*) Every vessel shall have due regard to the prevailing circumstances and conditions of restricted visibility when complying with the Rules of Section I of this Part.

(*d*) A vessel which detects by radar alone the presence of another vessel shall determine if a close-quarters situation is developing and/or risk of collision exists. If so, she shall take avoiding action in ample time, provided that when such action consists of an alteration of course, so far as possible the following shall be avoided:

(i) an alteration of course to port for a vessel forward of the beam, other than for a vessel being overtaken;

(ii) an alteration of course towards a vessel abeam or abaft the beam.

(*e*) Except where it has been determined that a risk of collision does not exist, every vessel which hears apparently forward of her beam the fog signal of another vessel, or which cannot avoid a close-quarters situation with another vessel forward of her beam, shall reduce her speed to the minimum at which she can be kept on her course. She shall if necessary take all her way off and in any event navigate with extreme caution until danger of collision is over.

PART C. LIGHTS AND SHAPES

Rule 20

Application

(*a*) Rules in this Part shall be complied with in all weathers.

(*b*) The Rules concerning lights shall be complied with from sunset to sunrise, and during such times no other lights shall be exhibited, except such lights as cannot be mistaken for the lights specified in these Rules or do not impair their visibility or distinctive character, or interfere with the keeping of a proper look-out.

(*c*) The lights prescribed by these Rules shall, if carried, also be exhibited from sunrise to sunset in restricted visibility and may be exhibited in all other circumstances when it is deemed necessary.

(*d*) The Rules concerning shapes shall be complied with by day.

(*e*) The lights and shapes specified in these Rules shall comply with the provisions of Annex I to these Regulations.

Rule 21

Definitions

(*a*) " Masthead light " means a white light placed over the fore and aft centreline of the vessel showing an unbroken light over an arc of the horizon of 225 degrees and so fixed as to show the light from right ahead to 22·5 degrees abaft the beam on either side of the vessel.

(*b*) " Sidelights " means a green light on the starboard side and a red light on the port side each showing an unbroken light over an arc of the horizon of 112·5 degrees and so fixed as to show the light from right ahead to 22·5 degrees abaft the beam on its respective side. In a vessel of less than 20 metres in length the sidelights may be combined in one lantern carried on the fore and aft centreline of the vessel.

(*c*) " Sternlight " means a white light placed as nearly as practicable at the stern showing an unbroken light over an arc of the horizon of 135 degrees and so fixed as to show the light 67·5 degrees from right aft on each side of the vessel.

(*d*) " Towing light " means a yellow light having the same characteristics as the " sternlight " defined in paragraph (*c*) of this Rule.

(*e*) "All round light " means a light showing an unbroken light over an arc of the horizon of 360 degrees.

(*f*) " Flashing light " means a light flashing at regular intervals at a frequency of 120 flashes or more per minute.

Rule 22
Visibility of lights

The lights prescribed in these Rules shall have an intensity as specified in Section 8 of Annex I to these Regulations so as to be visible at the following minimum ranges:

(*a*) In vessels of 50 metres or more in length:
  —a masthead light, 6 miles;
  —a sidelight, 3 miles;
  —a sternlight, 3 miles;
  —a towing light, 3 miles;
  —a white, red, green or yellow all-round light, 3 miles.

(*b*) In vessels of 12 metres or more in length but less than 50 metres in length:
  —a masthead light, 5 miles; except that where the length of the vessel is less than 20 metres, 3 miles;
  —a sidelight, 2 miles;
  —a sternlight, 2 miles;
  —a towing light, 2 miles;
  —a white, red, green or yellow all-round light, 2 miles.

(*c*) In vessels of less than 12 metres in length:
  —a masthead light, 2 miles;
  —a sidelight, 1 mile;
  —a sternlight, 2 miles;
  —a towing light, 2 miles;
  —a white, red, green or yellow all-round light, 2 miles.

(*d*) In inconspicuous, partly submerged vessels or objects being towed:
  —a white all-round light, 3 miles.

Rule 23

Power-driven vessels underway

(*a*) A power-driven vessel underway shall exhibit:
  (i) a masthead light forward;
  (ii) a second masthead light abaft of and higher than the forward one; except that a vessel of less than 50 metres in length shall not be obliged to exhibit such light but may do so;
  (iii) sidelights;
  (iv) a sternlight.

(*b*) An air-cushion vessel when operating in the non-displacement mode shall, in addition to the lights prescribed in paragraph (*a*) of this Rule, exhibit an all-round flashing yellow light.

(*c*) (i) A power-driven vessel of less than 12 metres in length may in lieu of the lights prescribed in paragraph (*a*) of this Rule exhibit an all-round white light and sidelights;
  (ii) a power-driven vessel of less than 7 metres in length whose maximum speed does not exceed 7 knots may in lieu of the lights prescribed in paragraph (*a*) of this Rule exhibit an all-round white light and shall, if practicable, also exhibit sidelights;
  (iii) the masthead light or all-round white light on a power-driven vessel of less than 12 metres in length may be displaced from the fore and aft centreline of the vessel if centreline fitting is not practicable, provided that the sidelights are combined in one lantern which shall be carried on the fore and aft centreline of the vessel or located as nearly as practicable in the same fore and aft line as the masthead light or the all-round white light.

Rule 24

Towing and pushing

(*a*) A power-driven vessel when towing shall exhibit:
  (i) instead of the light prescribed in Rule 23 (*a*) (i) or (*a*) (ii), two masthead lights in a vertical line. When the length of the tow, measuring from the stern of the towing vessel to the after end of the tow exceeds 200 metres, three such lights in a vertical line;
  (ii) sidelights;
  (iii) a sternlight;
  (iv) a towing light in a vertical line above the sternlight;
  (v) when the length of the tow exceeds 200 metres, a diamond shape where it can best be seen.

(*b*) When a pushing vessel and a vessel being pushed ahead are rigidly connected in a composite unit they shall be regarded as a power-driven vessel and exhibit the lights prescribed in Rule 23.

(c) A power-driven vessel when pushing ahead or towing alongside, except in the case of a composite unit, shall exhibit:

   (i) instead of the light prescribed in Rule 23 (a) (i) or (a) (ii), two masthead lights in a vertical line;

   (ii) sidelights;

   (iii) a sternlight.

(d) A power-driven vessel to which paragraph (a) or (c) of this Rule applies shall also comply with Rule 23 (a) (ii).

(e) A vessel or object being towed, other than those mentioned in paragraph (g) of this Rule, shall exhibit:

   (i) sidelights;

   (ii) a sternlight;

   (iii) when the length of the tow exceeds 200 metres, a diamond shape where it can best be seen.

(f) Provided that any number of vessels being towed alongside or pushed in a group shall be lighted as one vessel,

   (i) a vessel being pushed ahead, not being part of a composite unit, shall exhibit at the forward end, sidelights;

   (ii) a vessel being towed alongside shall exhibit a sternlight and at the forward end, sidelights.

(g) An inconspicuous, partly submerged vessel or object, or combination of such vessels or objects being towed, shall exhibit:

   (i) if it is less than 25 metres in breadth, one all-round white light at or near the forward end and one at or near the after end except that dracones need not exhibit a light at or near the forward end;

   (ii) if it is 25 metres or more in breadth, two additional all-round white lights at or near the extremities of its breadth;

   (iii) if it exceeds 100 metres in length, additional all-round white lights between the lights prescribed in sub-paragraphs (i) and (ii) so that the distance between the lights shall not exceed 100 metres;

   (iv) a diamond shape at or near the aftermost extremity of the last vessel or object being towed and if the length of the tow exceeds 200 metres an additional diamond shape where it can best be seen and located as far forward as is practicable.

(h) Where from any sufficient cause it is impracticable for a vessel or object being towed to exhibit the lights or shapes prescribed in paragraph (e) or (g) of this Rule, all possible measures shall be taken to light the vessel or object towed or at least to indicate the presence of such vessel or object.

(i) Where from any sufficient cause it is impracticable for a vessel not normally engaged in towing operations to display the lights prescribed in paragraph (a) or (c) of this Rule, such vessel shall not be required to exhibit those lights when engaged in towing another vessel in distress or otherwise in need of assistance. All possible measures shall be taken to indicate the nature of the relationship between the towing vessel and the vessel being towed as authorized by Rule 36, in particular by illuminating the towline.

RULE 25

Sailing vessels underway and vessels under oars

(a) A sailing vessel underway shall exhibit:
  (i) sidelights;
  (ii) a sternlight.

(b) In a sailing vessel of less than 20 metres in length the lights prescribed in paragraph (a) of this Rule may be combined in one lantern carried at or near the top of the mast where it can best be seen.

(c) A sailing vessel underway may, in addition to the lights prescribed in paragraph (a) of this Rule, exhibit at or near the top of the mast, where they can best be seen, two all-round lights in a vertical line, the upper being red and the lower green, but these lights shall not be exhibited in conjunction with the combined lantern permitted by paragraph (b) of this Rule.

(d) (i) A sailing vessel of less than 7 metres in length shall, if practicable, exhibit the lights prescribed in paragraphs (a) or (b) of this Rule, but if she does not, she shall have ready at hand an electric torch or lighted lantern showing a white light which shall be exhibited in sufficient time to prevent collision.

(ii) A vessel under oars may exhibit the lights prescribed in this Rule for sailing vessels, but if she does not, she shall have ready at hand an electric torch or lighted lantern showing a white light which shall be exhibited in sufficient time to prevent collision.

(e) A vessel proceeding under sail when also being propelled by machinery shall exhibit forward where it can best be seen a conical shape, apex downwards.

RULE 26

Fishing vessels

(a) A vessel engaged in fishing, whether underway or at anchor, shall exhibit only the lights and shapes prescribed in this Rule.

(b) A vessel when engaged in trawling, by which is meant the dragging through the water of a dredge net or other apparatus used as a fishing appliance, shall exhibit:
  (i) two all-round lights in a vertical line, the upper being green and the lower white, or a shape consisting of two cones with their apexes together in a vertical line one above the other; a vessel of less than 20 metres in length may instead of this shape exhibit a basket;
  (ii) a masthead light abaft of and higher than the all-round green light; a vessel of less than 50 metres in length shall not be obliged to exhibit such a light but may do so;
  (iii) when making way through the water, in addition to the lights prescribed in this paragraph, sidelights and a sternlight.

INTERNATIONAL REGULATIONS

(c) A vessel engaged in fishing, other than trawling, shall exhibit:

  (i) two all-round lights in a vertical line, the upper being red and the lower white, or a shape consisting of two cones with apexes together in a vertical line one above the other; a vessel of less than 20 metres in length may instead of this shape exhibit a basket;

 (ii) when there is outlying gear extending more than 150 metres horizontally from the vessel, an all-round white light or a cone apex upwards in the direction of the gear;

 (iii) when making way through the water, in addition to the lights prescribed in this paragraph, sidelights and a sternlight.

(d) A vessel engaged in fishing in close proximity to other vessels engaged in fishing may exhibit the additional signals described in Annex II to these Regulations.

(e) A vessel when not engaged in fishing shall not exhibit the lights or shapes prescribed in this Rule, but only those prescribed for a vessel of her length.

RULE 27

Vessels not under command or restricted in their ability to manoeuvre

(a) A vessel not under command shall exhibit:

  (i) two all-round red lights in a vertical line where they can best be seen;

 (ii) two balls or similar shapes in a vertical line where they can best be seen;

 (iii) when making way through the water, in addition to the lights prescribed in this paragraph, sidelights and a sternlight.

(b) A vessel restricted in her ability to manoeuvre, except a vessel engaged in mineclearance operations, shall exhibit:

  (i) three all-round lights in a vertical line where they can best be seen. The highest and lowest of these lights shall be red and the middle light shall be white;

 (ii) three shapes in a vertical line where they can best be seen. The highest and lowest of these shapes shall be balls and the middle one a diamond;

 (iii) when making way through the water, a masthead light or lights, sidelights and a sternlight, in addition to the lights prescribed in sub-paragraph (i);

 (iv) when at anchor, in addition to the lights or shapes prescribed in sub-paragraphs (i) and (ii), the light, lights or shape prescribed in Rule 30.

(c) A power-driven vessel engaged in a towing operation such as severely restricts the towing vessel and her tow in their ability to deviate from their course shall, in addition to the lights or shapes prescribed in Rule 24 (a), exhibit the lights or shapes prescribed in sub-paragraphs (b) (i) and (ii) of this Rule.

(d) A vessel engaged in dredging or underwater operations, when restricted in her ability to manoeuvre, shall exhibit the lights and shapes prescribed in sub-paragraphs (b) (i), (ii) and (iii) of this Rule and shall in addition, when obstruction exists, exhibit:

   (i) two all-round red lights or two balls in a vertical line to indicate the side on which the obstruction exists;

   (ii) two all-round green lights or two diamonds in a vertical line to indicate the side on which another vessel may pass;

   (iii) when at anchor, the lights or shapes prescribed in this paragraph instead of the lights or shape prescribed in Rule 30.

(e) Whenever the size of a vessel engaged in diving operations makes it impracticable to exhibit all lights and shapes prescribed in paragraph (d) of this Rule, the following shall be exhibited:

   (i) three all-round lights in a vertical line where they can best be seen. The highest and lowest of these lights shall be red and the middle light shall be white;

   (ii) a rigid replica of the International Code flag "A" not less than 1 metre in height. Measures shall be taken to ensure its all-round visibility.

(f) A vessel engaged in mineclearance operations shall in addition to the lights prescribed for a power-driven vessel in Rule 23 or to the lights or shape prescribed for a vessel at anchor in Rule 30 as appropriate, exhibit three all-round green lights or three balls. One of these lights or shapes shall be exhibited near the foremast head and one at each end of the fore yard. These lights or shapes indicate that it is dangerous for another vessel to approach within 1000 metres of the mineclearance vessel.

(g) Vessels of less than 12 metres in length, except those engaged in diving operations, shall not be required to exhibit the lights and shapes prescribed in this Rule.

(h) The signals prescribed in this Rule are not signals of vessels in distress and requiring assistance. Such signals are contained in Annex IV to these Regulations.

Rule 28

Vessels constrained by their draught

A vessel constrained by her draught may, in addition to the lights prescribed for power-driven vessels in Rule 23, exhibit where they can best be seen three all-round red lights in a vertical line, or a cylinder.

Rule 29

Pilot vessels

(a) A vessel engaged on pilotage duty shall exhibit:

   (i) at or near the masthead, two all-round lights in a vertical line, the upper being white and the lower red;

(ii) when underway, in addition, sidelights and a sternlight;

(iii) when at anchor, in addition to the lights prescribed in sub-paragraph (i), the light, lights or shape prescribed in Rule 30 for vessels at anchor.

(*b*) A pilot vessel when not engaged on pilotage duty shall exhibit the lights or shapes prescribed for a similar vessel of her length.

RULE 30

Anchored vessels and vessels aground

(*a*) A vessel at anchor shall exhibit where it can best be seen:

(i) in the fore part, an all-round white light or one ball;

(ii) at or near the stern and at a lower level than the light prescribed in sub-paragraph (i), an all-round white light.

(*b*) A vessel of less than 50 metres in length may exhibit an all-round white light where it can best be seen instead of the lights prescribed in paragraph (*a*) of this Rule.

(*c*) A vessel at anchor may, and a vessel of 100 metres and more in length shall, also use the available working or equivalent lights to illuminate her decks.

(*d*) A vessel aground shall exhibit the lights prescribed in paragraphs (*a*) or (*b*) of this Rule and in addition, where they can best be seen:

(i) two all-round red lights in a vertical line;

(ii) three balls in a vertical line.

(*e*) A vessel of less than 7 metres in length, when at anchor, not in or near a narrow channel, fairway or anchorage, or where other vessels normally navigate, shall not be required to exhibit the lights or shapes prescribed in paragraphs (*a*) and (*b*) of this Rule.

(*f*) A vessel of less than 12 metres in length, when aground, shall not be required to exhibit the lights or shapes prescribed in sub-paragraphs (*d*) (i) and (ii) of this Rule.

RULE 31

Seaplanes

Where it is impracticable for a seaplane to exhibit lights and shapes of the characteristics or in the positions prescribed in the Rules of this Part she shall exhibit lights and shapes as closely similar in characteristics and position as is possible.

PART D. SOUND AND LIGHT SIGNALS

RULE 32

Definitions

(a) The word " whistle " means any sound signalling appliance capable of producing the prescribed blasts and which complies with the specifications in Annex III to these Regulations.

(b) The term " short blast " means a blast of about one second's duration.

(c) The term " prolonged blast " means a blast of from four to six seconds' duration.

RULE 33

Equipment for sound signals

(a) A vessel of 12 metres or more in length shall be provided with a whistle and a bell and a vessel of 100 metres or more in length shall, in addition, be provided with a gong, the tone and sound of which cannot be confused with that of the bell. The whistle, bell and gong shall comply with the specifications in Annex III to these Regulations. The bell or gong or both may be replaced by other equipment having the same respective sound characteristics, provided that manual sounding of the prescribed signals shall always be possible.

(b) A vessel of less than 12 metres in length shall not be obliged to carry the sound signalling appliances prescribed in paragraph (a) of this Rule but if she does not, she shall be provided with some other means of making an efficient sound signal.

RULE 34

Manoeuvring and warning signals

(a) When vessels are in sight of one another, a power-driven vessel underway, when manoeuvring as authorized or required by these Rules, shall indicate that manoeuvre by the following signals on her whistle:

—one short blast to mean " I am altering my course to starboard ";

—two short blasts to mean " I am altering my course to port ";

—three short blasts to mean " I am operating astern propulsion ".

(b) Any vessel may supplement the whistle signals prescribed in paragraph (a) of this Rule by light signals, repeated as appropriate, whilst the manoeuvre is being carried out:

(i) these light signals shall have the following significance:

—one flash to mean " I am altering my course to starboard ";

—two flashes to mean " I am altering my course to port ";

—three flashes to mean " I am operating astern propulsion ";

(ii) the duration of each flash shall be about one second, the interval between flashes shall be about one second, and the interval between successive signals shall be not less than ten seconds;

(iii) the light used for this signal shall, if fitted, be an all-round white light, visible at a minimum range of 5 miles, and shall comply with the provisions of Annex I to these Regulations.

(c) When in sight of one another in a narrow channel or fairway:

(i) a vessel intending to overtake another shall in compliance with Rule 9 (e) (i) indicate her intention by the following signals on her whistle:
—two prolonged blasts followed by one short blast to mean " I intend to overtake you on your starboard side ";
—two prolonged blasts followed by two short blasts to mean " I intend to overtake you on your port side ".

(ii) the vessel about to be overtaken when acting in accordance with Rule 9 (e) (i) shall indicate her agreement by the following signal on her whistle:
—one prolonged, one short, one prolonged and one short blast, in that order.

(d) When vessels in sight of one another are approaching each other and from any cause either vessel fails to understand the intentions or actions of the other, or is in doubt whether sufficient action is being taken by the other to avoid collision, the vessel in doubt shall immediately indicate such doubt by giving at least five short and rapid blasts on the whistle. Such signal may be supplemented by a light signal of at least five short and rapid flashes.

(e) A vessel nearing a bend or an area of a channel or fairway where other vessels may be obscured by an intervening obstruction shall sound one prolonged blast. Such signal shall be answered with a prolonged blast by any approaching vessel that may be within hearing around the bend or behind the intervening obstruction.

(f) If whistles are fitted on a vessel at a distance apart of more than 100 metres, one whistle only shall be used for giving manoeuvring and warning signals.

RULE 35

Sound signals in restricted visibility

In or near an area of restricted visibility, whether by day or night, the signals prescribed in this Rule shall be used as follows:

(a) A power-driven vessel making way through the water shall sound at intervals of not more than 2 minutes one prolonged blast.

(b) A power-driven vessel underway but stopped and making no way through the water shall sound at intervals of not more than 2 minutes two prolonged blasts in succession with an interval of about 2 seconds between them.

(c) A vessel not under command, a vessel restricted in her ability to manoeuvre, a vessel constrained by her draught, a sailing vessel, a vessel engaged in fishing and a vessel engaged in towing or pushing another vessel shall, instead of the signals prescribed in paragraphs (a) or (b) of this Rule, sound at intervals of not more than 2 minutes three blasts in succession, namely one prolonged followed by two short blasts.

(d) A vessel engaged in fishing, when at anchor, and a vessel restricted in her ability to manoeuvre when carrying out her work at anchor, shall instead of the signals prescribed in paragraph (g) of this Rule sound the signal prescribed in paragraph (c) of this Rule.

(e) A vessel towed or if more than one vessel is towed the last vessel of the tow, if manned, shall at intervals of not more than 2 minutes sound four blasts in succession, namely one prolonged followed by three short blasts. When practicable, this signal shall be made immediately after the signal made by the towing vessel.

(f) When a pushing vessel and a vessel being pushed ahead are rigidly connected in a composite unit they shall be regarded as a power-driven vessel and shall give the signals prescribed in paragraphs (a) or (b) of this Rule.

(g) A vessel at anchor shall at intervals of not more than one minute ring the bell rapidly for about 5 seconds. In a vessel of 100 metres or more in length the bell shall be sounded in the forepart of the vessel and immediately after the ringing of the bell the gong shall be sounded rapidly for about 5 seconds in the after part of the vessel. A vessel at anchor may in addition sound three blasts in succession, namely one short, one prolonged and one short blast, to give warning of her position and of the possibility of collision to an approaching vessel.

(h) A vessel aground shall give the bell signal and if required the gong signal prescribed in paragraph (g) of this Rule and shall, in addition, give three separate and distinct strokes on the bell immediately before and after the rapid ringing of the bell. A vessel aground may in addition sound an appropriate whistle signal.

(i) A vessel of less than 12 metres in length shall not be obliged to give the above-mentioned signals but, if she does not, shall make some other efficient sound signal at intervals of not more than 2 minutes.

(j) A pilot vessel when engaged on pilotage duty may in addition to the signals prescribed in paragraphs (a), (b) or (g) of this Rule sound an identity signal consisting of four short blasts.

Rule 36
Signals to attract attention

If necessary to attract the attention of another vessel any vessel may make light or sound signals that cannot be mistaken for any signal authorized elsewhere in these Rules, or may direct the beam of her searchlight in the direction of the danger, in such a way as not to embarrass any vessel.

Any light to attract the attention of another vessel shall be such that it cannot be mistaken for any aid to navigation. For the purpose of this Rule the use of high intensity intermittent or revolving lights, such as strobe lights, shall be avoided.

Rule 37
Distress signals

When a vessel is in distress and requires assistance she shall use or exhibit the signals described in Annex IV to these Regulations.

PART E. EXEMPTIONS

RULE 38

Exemptions

Any vessel (or class of vessels) provided that she complies with the requirements of the International Regulations for Preventing Collisions at Sea, 1960, the keel of which is laid or which is at a corresponding stage of construction before the entry into force of these Regulations may be exempted from compliance therewith as follows:

(a) The installation of lights with ranges prescribed in Rule 22, until four years after the date of entry into force of these Regulations.

(b) The installation of lights with colour specifications as prescribed in Section 7 of Annex I to these Regulations, until four years after the date of entry into force of these Regulations.

(c) The repositioning of lights as a result of conversion from Imperial to metric units and rounding off measurement figures, permanent exemption.

(d) (i) The repositioning of masthead lights on vessels of less than 150 metres in length, resulting from the prescriptions of Section 3 (a) of Annex I to these Regulations, permanent exemption.

    (ii) The repositioning of masthead lights on vessels of 150 metres or more in length, resulting from the prescriptions of Section 3 (a) of Annex I to these Regulations, until nine years after the date of entry into force of these Regulations.

(e) The repositioning of masthead lights resulting from the prescriptions of Section 2 (b) of Annex I , to these Regulations until nine years after the date of entry into force of these Regulations.

(f) The repositioning of sidelights resulting from the prescriptions of Sections 2 (g) and 3 (b) of Annex I to these Regulations until nine years after the date of entry into force of these Regulations

(g) The requirements for sound signal appliances prescribed in Annex III, to these Regulations until nine years after the date of entry into force of these Regulations.

(h) The repositioning of all-round lights resulting from the prescription of Section 9 (b) of Annex I to these Regulations, permanent exemption.

ANNEX I

Positioning and technical details of lights and shapes

1. *Definition*

The term " height above the hull " means height above the uppermost continuous deck. This height shall be measured from the position vertically beneath the location of the light.

2. Vertical positioning and spacing of lights

(a) On a power-driven vessel of 20 metres or more in length the masthead lights shall be placed as follows:

    (i) the forward masthead light, or if only one masthead light is carried, then that light, at a height above the hull of not less than 6 metres, and, if the breadth of the vessel exceeds 6 metres, then at a height above the hull not less than such breadth, so however that the light need not be placed at a greater height above the hull than 12 metres;

    (ii) when two masthead lights are carried the after one shall be at least 4·5 metres vertically higher than the forward one.

(b) The vertical separation of masthead lights of power-driven vessels shall be such that in all normal conditions of trim the after light will be seen over and separate from the forward light at a distance of 1,000 metres from the stem when viewed from sea level.

(c) The masthead light of a power-driven vessel of 12 metres but less than 20 metres in length shall be placed at a height above the gunwale of not less than 2·5 metres.

(d) A power-driven vessel of less than 12 metres in length may carry the uppermost light at a height of less than 2·5 metres above the gunwale. When however a masthead light is carried in addition to sidelights and a sternlight, then such masthead light shall be carried at least 1 metre higher than the sidelights.

(e) One of the two or three masthead lights prescribed for a power-driven vessel when engaged in towing or pushing another vessel shall be placed in the same position as either the forward masthead light or the after masthead light; provided that, if carried on the aftermast, the lowest after masthead light shall be at least 4·5 metres vertically higher than the forward masthead light.

(f) (i) The masthead light or lights prescribed in Rule 23 (a) shall be so placed as to be above and clear of all other lights and obstructions except as described in sub-paragraph (ii).

    (ii) When it is impracticable to carry the all-round lights prescribed by Rule 27 (b) (i) or Rule 28 below the masthead lights, they may be carried above the after masthead light(s) or vertically in between the forward masthead light(s) and after masthead light(s), provided that in the latter case the requirement of Section 3 (c) of this Annex shall be complied with.

(g) The sidelights of a power-driven vessel shall be placed at a height above the hull not greater than three-quarters of that of the forward masthead light. They shall not be so low as to be interfered with by deck lights.

(h) The sidelights, if in a combined lantern and carried on a power-driven vessel of less than 20 metres in length, shall be placed not less than 1 metre below the masthead light.

(i) When the Rules prescribe two or three lights to be carried in a vertical line, they shall be spaced as follows:

(i) on a vessel of 20 metres in length or more such lights shall be spaced not less than 2 metres apart, and the lowest of these lights shall, except where a towing light is required, be placed at a height of not less than 4 metres above the hull.

(ii) on a vessel of less than 20 metres in length such lights shall be spaced not less than 1 metre apart and the lowest of these lights shall, except where a towing light is required, be placed at a height of not less than 2 metres above the hull.

(iii) when three lights are carried they shall be equally spaced.

(*j*) The lower of the two all-round lights prescribed for a vessel when engaged in fishing shall be at a height above the sidelights not less than twice the distance between the two vertical lights.

(*k*) The forward anchor light prescribed in Rule 30 (*a*) (i), when two are carried, shall not be less than 4·5 metres above the after one. On a vessel of 50 metres or more in length this forward anchor light shall be placed at a height of not less than 6 metres above the hull.

3. *Horizontal positioning and spacing of lights*

(*a*) When two masthead lights are prescribed for a power-driven vessel, the horizontal distance between them shall not be less than one-half of the length of the vessel but need not be more than 100 metres. The forward light shall be placed not more than one-quarter of the length of the vessel from the stem.

(*b*) On a power-driven vessel of 20 metres or more in length the sidelights shall not be placed in front of the forward masthead lights. They shall be placed at or near the side of the vessel.

(*c*) When the lights prescribed in Rule 27 (*b*) (i) or Rule 28 are placed vertically between the forward masthead light(s) and the after masthead light(s) these all-round lights shall be placed at a horizontal distance of not less than 2 metres from the fore and aft centreline of the vessel in the athwartship direction.

4. *Details of location of direction-indicating lights for fishing vessels, dredgers and vessels engaged in underwater operations*

(*a*) The light indicating the direction of the outlying gear from a vessel engaged in fishing as prescribed in Rule 26 (*c*) (ii) shall be placed at a horizontal distance of not less than 2 metres and not more than 6 metres away from the two all-round red and white lights. This light shall be placed not higher than the all-round white light prescribed in Rule 26 (*c*) (i) and not lower than the sidelights.

(*b*) The lights and shapes on a vessel engaged in dredging or underwater operations to indicate the obstructed side and/or the side on which it is safe to pass, as prescribed in Rule 27 (*d*) (i) and (ii), shall be placed at the maximum practical horizontal distance, but in no case less than 2 metres, from the lights or shapes prescribed in Rule 27 (*b*) (i) and (ii). In no case shall the upper of these lights or shapes be at a greater height than the lower of the three lights or shapes prescribed in Rule 27 (*b*) (i) and (ii).

5. Screens for sidelights

The sidelights of vessels of 20 metres or more in length shall be fitted with inboard screens painted matt black, and meeting the requirements of Section 9 of this Annex. On vessels of less than 20 metres in length the side-lights, if necessary to meet the requirements of Section 9 of this Annex, shall be fitted with inboard matt black screens. With a combined lantern, using a single vertical filament and a very narrow division between the green and red sections, external screens need not be fitted.

6. Shapes

(a) Shapes shall be black and of the following sizes:

(i) a ball shall have a diameter of not less than 0.6 metre;

(ii) a cone shall have a base diameter of not less than 0.6 metre and a height equal to its diameter;

(iii) a cylinder shall have a diameter of at least 0.6 metre and a height of twice its diameter;

(iv) a diamond shape shall consist of two cones as defined in (ii) above having a common base.

(b) The vertical distance between shapes shall be at least 1.5 metres.

(c) In a vessel of less than 20 metres in length shapes of lesser dimensions but commensurate with the size of the vessel may be used and the distance apart may be correspondingly reduced.

7. Colour specification of lights

The chromaticity of all navigation lights shall conform to the following standards, which lie within the boundaries of the area of the diagram specified for each colour by the International Commission on Illumination (CIE).

The boundaries of the area for each colour are given by indicating the corner co-ordinates, which are as follows:

(i) *White*

x	0.525	0.525	0.452	0.310	0.310	0.443
y	0.382	0.440	0.440	0.348	0.283	0.382

(ii) *Green*

x	0.028	0.009	0.300	0.203
y	0.385	0.723	0.511	0.356

(iii) *Red*

x	0.680	0.660	0.735	0.721
y	0.320	0.320	0.265	0.259

(iv) *Yellow*

x	0.612	0.618	0.575	0.575
y	0.382	0.382	0.425	0.406

8. *Intensity of lights*

(*a*) The minimum luminous intensity of lights shall be calculated by using the formula:

$$I = 3 \cdot 43 \times 10^6 \times T \times D^2 \times K^{-D}$$

where I is luminous intensity in candelas under service conditions,

     T is threshold factor 2×10^{-7} lux,

     D is range of visibility (luminous range) of the light in nautical miles,

     K is atmospheric transmissivity.

     For prescribed lights the value of K shall be $0 \cdot 8$, corresponding to a meteorological visibility of approximately 13 nautical miles.

(*b*) A selection of figures derived from the formula is given in the following table:

Range of visibility (luminous range) of light in nautical miles D	Luminous intensity of light in candelas for $K = 0 \cdot 8$ I
1	$0 \cdot 9$
2	$4 \cdot 3$
3	12
4	27
5	52
6	94

Note: The maximum luminous intensity of navigation lights should be limited to avoid undue glare. This shall not be achieved by a variable control of the luminous intensity.

9. *Horizontal sectors*

(*a*) (i) In the forward direction, sidelights as fitted on the vessel shall show the minimum required intensities. The intensities must decrease to reach practical cut-off between 1 degree and 3 degrees outside the prescribed sectors.

(ii) For sternlights and masthead lights and at $22 \cdot 5$ degrees abaft the beam for sidelights, the minimum required intensities shall be maintained over the arc of the horizon up to 5 degrees within the limits of the sectors prescribed in Rule 21. From 5 degrees within the prescribed sectors the intensity may decrease by 50 per cent up to the prescribed limits; it shall decrease steadily to reach practical cut-off at not more than 5 degrees outside the prescribed sectors.

(*b*) All-round lights shall be so located as not to be obscured by masts, topmasts or structures within angular sectors of more than 6 degrees, except anchor lights prescribed in Rule 30, which need not be placed at an impracticable height above the hull.

10. *Vertical sectors*

(*a*) The vertical sectors of electric lights as fitted, with the exception of lights on sailing vessels shall ensure that:

  (i) at least the required minimum intensity is maintained at all angles from 5 degrees above to 5 degrees below the horizontal;

  (ii) at least 60 per cent of the required minimum intensity is maintained from 7·5 degrees above to 7·5 degrees below the horizontal.

(*b*) In the case of sailing vessels the vertical sectors of electric lights as fitted shall ensure that:

  (i) at least the required minimum intensity is maintained at all angles from 5 degrees above to 5 degrees below the horizontal;

  (ii) at least 50 per cent of the required minimum intensity is maintained from 25 degrees above to 25 degrees below the horizontal.

(*c*) In the case of lights other than electric these specifications shall be met as closely as possible.

11. *Intensity of non-electric lights*

Non-electric lights shall so far as practicable comply with the minimum intensities, as specified in the Table given in Section 8 of this Annex.

12. *Manoeuvring light*

Notwithstanding the provisions of paragraph 2 (*f*) of this Annex the manoeuvring light described in Rule 34 (*b*) shall be placed in the same fore and aft vertical plane as the masthead light or lights and, where practicable, at a minimum height of 2 metres vertically above the forward masthead light, provided that it shall be carried not less than 2 metres vertically above or below the after masthead light. On a vessel where only one masthead light is carried, the manoeuvring light, if fitted, shall be carried where it can best be seen, not less than 2 metres vertically apart from the masthead light.

13. *Approval*

The construction of lights and shapes and the installation of lights on board the vessel shall be to the satisfaction of the appropriate authority of the State whose flag the vessel is entitled to fly.

ANNEX II

Additional signals for fishing vessels fishing in close proximity

1. *General*

The lights mentioned herein shall, if exhibited in pursuance of Rule 26 (*d*). be placed where they can best be seen. They shall be at least 0·9 metre apart but at a lower level than lights prescribed in Rule 26 (*b*) (i) and (*c*) (i). The lights shall be visible all round the horizon at a distance of at least 1 mile but at a lesser distance than the lights prescribed by these Rules for fishing vessels.

2. *Signals for trawlers*

(*a*) Vessels when engaged in trawling, whether using demersal or pelagic gear, may exhibit:

   (i) when shooting their nets:
      two white lights in a vertical line;
  (ii) when hauling their nets:
      one white light over one red light in a vertical line;
 (iii) when the net has come fast upon an obstruction:
      two red lights in a vertical line.

(*b*) Each vessel engaged in pair trawling may exhibit:

   (i) by night, a searchlight directed forward and in the direction of the other vessel of the pair;
  (ii) when shooting or hauling their nets or when their nets have come fast upon an obstruction, the lights prescribed in 2 (*a*) above.

3. *Signals for purse seiners*

Vessels engaged in fishing with purse seine gear may exhibit two yellow lights in a vertical line. These lights shall flash alternately every second and with equal light and occultation duration. These lights may be exhibited only when the vessel is hampered by its fishing gear.

ANNEX III

Technical details of sound signal appliances

1. *Whistles*

(*a*) *Frequencies and range of audibility*

The fundamental frequency of the signal shall lie within the range 70–700 Hz.

The range of audibility of the signal from a whistle shall be determined by those frequencies, which may include the fundamental and/or one or more higher frequencies, which lie within the range 180–700 Hz ($\pm$ 1 per cent) and which provide the sound pressure levels specified in paragraph 1 (*c*) below.

(*b*) *Limits of fundamental frequencies*

To ensure a wide variety of whistle characteristics, the fundamental frequency of a whistle shall be between the following limits:

   (i) 70–200 Hz, for a vessel 200 metres or more in length;
  (ii) 130–350 Hz, for a vessel 75 metres but less than 200 metres in length;
 (iii) 250–700 Hz, for a vessel less than 75 metres in length.

(c) *Sound signal intensity and range of audibility*

A whistle fitted in a vessel shall provide, in the direction of maximum intensity of the whistle and at a distance of 1 metre from it, a sound pressure level in at least one 1/3rd-octave band within the range of frequencies 180–700 Hz ($\pm$ 1 per cent) of not less than the appropriate figure given in the table below.

Length of vessel in metres	*1/3rd-octave band level at 1 metre in dB referred to $2 \times 10^{-5}\ N/m^2$*	*Audibility range in nautical miles*
200 or more	143	2
75 but less than 200 ...	138	1·5
20 but less than 75 ...	130	1
Less than 20	120	0·5

The range of audibility in the table above is for information and is approximately the range at which a whistle may be heard on its forward axis with 90 per cent probability in conditions of still air on board a vessel having average background noise level at the listening posts (taken to be 68 dB in the octave band centred on 250 Hz and 63 dB in the octave band centred on 500 Hz).

In practice the range at which a whistle may be heard is extremely variable and depends critically on weather conditions; the values given can be regarded as typical but under conditions of strong wind or high ambient noise level at the listening post the range may be much reduced.

(d) *Directional properties*

The sound pressure level of a directional whistle shall be not more than 4 dB below the prescribed sound pressure level on the axis at any direction in the horizontal plane within $\pm$ 45 degrees of the axis. The sound pressure level at any other direction in the horizontal plane shall be not more than 10 dB below the prescribed sound pressure level on the axis, so that the range in any direction will be at least half the range on the forward axis. The sound pressure level shall be measured in that 1/3rd-octave band which determines the audibility range.

(e) *Positioning of whistles*

When a directional whistle is to be used as the only whistle on a vessel, it shall be installed with its maximum intensity directed straight ahead.

A whistle shall be placed as high as practicable on a vessel, in order to reduce interception of the emitted sound by obstructions and also to minimize hearing damage risk to personnel. The sound pressure level of the vessel's own signal at listening posts shall not exceed 110 dB (A) and so far as practicable should not exceed 100 dB (A).

(f) *Fitting of more than one whistle*

If whistles are fitted at a distance apart of more than 100 metres, it shall be so arranged that they are not sounded simultaneously.

(g) Combined whistle systems

If due to the presence of obstructions the sound field of a single whistle or of one of the whistles referred to in paragraph 1 (*f*) above is likely to have a zone of greatly reduced signal level, it is recommended that a combined whistle system be fitted so as to overcome this reduction. For the purposes of the Rules a combined whistle system is to be regarded as a single whistle. The whistles of a combined system shall be located at a distance apart of not more than 100 metres and arranged to be sounded simultaneously. The frequency of any one whistle shall differ from those of the others by at least 10 Hz.

2. Bell or gong

(a) Intensity of signal

A bell or gong, or other device having similar sound characteristics shall produce a sound pressure level of not less than 110 dB at a distance of 1 metre from it.

(b) Construction

Bells and gongs shall be made of corrosion-resistant material and designed to give a clear tone. The diameter of the mouth of the bell shall be not less than 300 mm for vessels of 20 metres or more in length, and shall be not less than 200 mm for vessels of 12 metres or more but of less than 20 metres in length. Where practicable, a power-driven bell striker is recommended to ensure constant force but manual operation shall be possible. The mass of the striker shall be not less than 3 per cent of the mass of the bell.

3. Approval

The construction of sound signal appliances, their performance and their installation on board the vessel shall be to the satisfaction of the appropriate authority of the State whose flag the vessel is entitled to fly.

ANNEX IV

Distress signals

1.   The following signals, used or exhibited either together or separately, indicate distress and need of assistance:

   (a)   a gun or other explosive signal fired at intervals of about a minute;

   (b)   a continuous sounding with any fog-signalling apparatus;

   (c)   rockets or shells, throwing red stars fired one at a time at short intervals;

   (d)   a signal made by radiotelegraphy or by any other signalling method consisting of the group · · · − − − · · · (SOS) in the Morse Code;

(e)   a signal sent by radiotelephony consisting of the spoken word
"Mayday";

(f)   the International Code Signal of distress indicated by N.C.;

(g)   a signal consisting of a square flag having above or below it a ball or
anything resembling a ball;

(h)   flames on the vessel (as from a burning tar barrel, oil barrel, etc.);

(i)   a rocket parachute flare or a hand flare showing a red light;

(j)   a smoke signal giving off orange-coloured smoke;

(k)   slowly and repeatedly raising and lowering arms outstretched to each
side;

(l)   the radiotelegraph alarm signal;

(m)   the radiotelephone alarm signal;

(n)   signals transmitted by emergency position-indicating radio beacons.

2.   The use of exhibition of any of the foregoing signals except for the
purpose of indicating distress and need of assistance and the use of other
signals which may be confused with any of the above signals is prohibited.

3.   Attention is drawn to the relevant sections of the International Code
of Signals, the Merchant Ship Search and Rescue Manual and the following
signals:

(a)   a piece of orange-coloured canvas with either a black square and circle
or other appropriate symbol (for identification from the air);

(b)   a dye marker.

RULE OF THE ROAD AT SEA

SAILING the seas every moment of the day and night are vessels of many types and nationalities, the high-speed liners, the vessels carrying cargo to distant parts, the fishing vessels engaged in their work earning a living from the sea, the tug towing a disabled vessel, cable ships repairing a cable, ships of war recovering aircraft or engaged in minesweeping, all carrying on in their own particular sphere.

Around the coasts or on the wide expansive oceans, wherever the demands of commerce require transportation of commodities, it is inevitable that the course of vessels must cross, the high-speed vessel overtakes the slow vessel, and thus unavoidably create circumstances involving risk of collision. If this catastrophe is to be avoided, or at least the risk reduced to a minimum, it is imperative that vessels adhere to definite rules under which the responsibility of avoiding collision rests with a particular vessel.

Such rules have been formulated, are international in character since they apply to ships of all maritime nations and are incorporated in thirty-eight Rules and four Annexes entitled 'International Regulations for Preventing Collisions at Sea', 1972.

During daytime in clear weather the type of vessel being met and her course are easily ascertained, and the correct action for the giving way vessel readily determined. In the darkness of the night, however, visibility is limited, and without a recognised system of illumination the nature of an approaching vessel could not with any degree of certainty be predicted.

With the object of indicating to those in charge of a vessel

5

the type of craft within their view, under the Regulations, vessels according to their class are compelled to exhibit certain lights which show over specified arcs, thus an observer can tell whether an approaching vessel is a power-driven vessel, sailing vessel, trawler, etc.

The Regulations provide for the conduct of a vessel in fog. When this condition prevails visibility is restricted, and warning of approach is given by signals made on the whistle, or fog horn.

A grave responsibility rests upon those in charge of a vessel at sea, and the object of this work is to assist those who aspire to such a position to acquire a comprehensive knowledge of the information necessary to prove they are fully competent to perform the duties on, and take the control of, a vessel's bridge, so far as the Rule of the Road at Sea applies.

The first step is, naturally, to understand the Regulations for Preventing Collisions at Sea, which, as already mentioned, consists of 38 Rules. These Rules are divided into:—

Part A—General.

Part B—Steering and Sailing Rules.

Part C—Lights and Shapes.

Part D—Sound and Light Signals.

Part E—Exemptions.

Annex I—Positioning and Technical Details of Lights and Shapes.

Annex II—Additional Signals for Fishing Vessels in close Proximity.

Annex III—Technical Details of Sound Signalling Appliances.

Annex IV—Distress Signals.

INTERNATIONAL REGULATIONS FOR PREVENTING COLLISIONS AT SEA, 1972

PART A. GENERAL

RULE 1

Application

(*a*) These Rules shall apply to all vessels upon the high seas and in all waters connected therewith navigable by seagoing vessels.

(*b*) Nothing in these Rules shall interfere with the operation of special rules made by an appropriate authority for roadsteads, harbours, rivers, lakes or inland waterways connected with the high seas and navigable by seagoing vessels. Such special rules shall conform as closely as possible to these Rules.

(*c*) Nothing in these Rules shall interfere with the operation of any special rules made by the Government of any State with respect to additional station or signal lights or whistle signals for ships of war and vessels proceeding under convoy, or with respect to additional station or signal lights for fishing vessels engaged in fishing as a fleet. These additional station or signal lights or whistle signals shall, so far as possible, be such that they cannot be mistaken for any light or signal authorised elsewhere under these Rules.

(*d*) Traffic separation schemes may be adopted by the Organisation for the purpose of these Rules.

e) Whenever the Government concerned shall have determined that a vessel of special construction or purpose cannot comply fully with the provisions of any of these Rules with respect to the number, position, range or arc of visibility

of lights or shapes, as well as to the disposition and characteristics of sound-signalling appliances, without interfering with
the special function of the vessel, such vessel shall comply with
such other provisions in regard to the number, position, range
or arc of visibility of lights or shapes, as well as to the disposition and characteristics of sound-signalling appliances, as
her Government shall have determined to be the closest
possible compliance with these Rules in respect to that vessel.

Rule 2

Responsibility

(*a*) Nothing in these Rules shall exonerate any vessel, or
the owner, master or crew thereof, from the consequences of
any neglect to comply with these Rules or of the neglect of any
precaution which may be required by the ordinary practice of
seamen, or by the special circumstances of the case.

(*b*) In construing and complying with these Rules due
regard shall be had to all dangers of navigation and collision
and to any special circumstances, including the limitations of
the vessels involved, which may make a departure from these
Rules necessary to avoid immediate danger.

Rule 3

General definitions

For the purposes of these Rules, except where the context
otherwise requires:—

(*a*) The word 'vessel' includes every description of water
   craft, including non-displacement craft and seaplanes,
   used or capable of being used as a means of transportation on water.

(*b*) The term 'power-driven vessel' means any vessel propelled by machinery.

(*c*) The term 'sailing vessel' means any vessel under sail provided that propelling machinery, if fitted, is not being used.

(*d*) The term 'vessel engaged in fishing' means any vessel fishing with nets, lines, trawls or other fishing apparatus which restrict manoeuvrability, but does not include a vessel fishing with trolling lines or other fishing apparatus which do not restrict manoeuvrability.

(*e*) The word 'seaplane' includes any aircraft designed to manoeuvre on the water.

(*f*) The term 'vessel not under command' means a vessel which through some exceptional circumstances is unable to manoeuvre as required by these Rules and is therefore unable to keep out of the way of another vessel.

(*g*) The term 'vessel restricted in her ability to manoeuvre' means a vessel which from the nature of her work is restricted in her ability to manoeuvre as required by these Rules and is therefore unable to keep out of the way of another vessel.

The following vessels shall be regarded as vessels restricted in their ability to manoeuvre:

(i) a vessel engaged in laying, servicing or picking up a navigation mark, submarine cable or pipeline;

(ii) a vessel engaged in dredging, surveying or underwater operations;

(iii) a vessel engaged in replenishment or transferring persons, provisions or cargo while underway;

(iv) a vessel engaged in the launching or recovery of aircraft;

(v) a vessel engaged in minesweeping operations;
(vi) a vessel engaged in a towing operation such as severely restricts the towing vessel and her tow in their ability to deviate from their course.

(*h*) The term 'vessel constrained by her draught' means a power-driven vessel which because of her draught in relation to the available depth of water is severely restricted in her ability to deviate from the course she is following.

(*i*) The word 'underway' means that a vessel is not at anchor, or made fast to the shore, or aground.

(*j*) The words 'length' and 'breadth' of a vessel mean her length overall and greatest breadth.

(*k*) Vessels shall be deemed to be in sight of one another only when one can be observed visually from the other.

(*l*) The term 'restricted visibility' means any condition in which visibility is restricted by fog, mist, falling snow, heavy rainstorms, sandstorms or any other similar causes.

PART B. STEERING AND SAILING RULES

Section 1. Conduct of vessels in any condition of visibility

RULE 4

Application

Rules in this Section apply in any condition of visibility.

RULE 5

Look-out

Every vessel shall at all times maintain a proper look-out by sight and hearing as well as by all available means appropriate in the prevailing circumstances and conditions so as to make a full appraisal of the situation and of the risk of collision.

RULE 6

Safe speed

Every vessel shall at all times proceed at a safe speed so that she can take proper and effective action to avoid collision and be stopped within a distance appropriate to the prevailing circumstances and conditions.

In determining a safe speed the following factors shall be among those taken into account:—

(*a*) By all vessels:—

    (i) the state of visibility;

    (ii) the traffic density, including concentrations of fishing vessels or any other vessels;

    (iii) the manoeuvrability of the vessel with special reference to stopping distance and turning ability in the prevailing conditions;

    (iv) at night the presence of background light such as from shore lights or from back scatter of her own lights;

    (v) the state of wind, sea and current, and the proximity of navigational hazards;

    (vi) the draught in relation to the available depth of water.

(*b*) Additionally, by vessels with operational radar:

   (i) the characteristics, efficiency and limitations of the radar equipment;

  (ii) any constraints imposed by the radar range scale in use;

 (iii) the effect on radar detection of the sea state, weather and other sources of interference;

 (iv) the possibility that small vessels, ice and other floating objects may not be detected by radar at an adequate range;

  (v) the number, location and movement of vessels detected by radar;

 (vi) the more exact assessment of the visibility that may be possible when radar is used to determine the range of vessels or other objects in the vicinity.

RULE 7

Risk of collision

(*a*) Every vessel shall use all available means appropriate to the prevailing circumstances and conditions to determine if risk of collision exists. If there is any doubt such risk shall be deemed to exist.

(*b*) Proper use shall be made of radar equipment if fitted and operational, including long-range scanning to obtain early warning of risk of collision and radar plotting or equivalent systematic observation of detected objects.

(*c*) Assumption shall not be made on the basis of scanty information, especially scanty radar information.

(*d*) In determining if risk of collision exists the following considerations shall be among those taken into account:—

  (i) such risk shall be deemed to exist if the compass

bearing of an approaching vessel does not appreciably change;

(ii) such risk may sometimes exist even when an appreciable bearing change is evident, particularly when approaching a very large vessel or a tow or when approaching a vessel at close range.

RULE 8

Action to avoid collision

(*a*) Any action taken to avoid collision shall, if the circumstances of the case admit, be positive, made in ample time and with due regard to the observance of good seamanship.

(*b*) Any alteration of course and/or speed to avoid collision shall, if the circumstances of the case admit, be large enough to be readily apparent to another vessel observing visually or by radar; a succession of small alterations of course and/or speed should be avoided.

(*c*) If there is sufficient sea room, alteration of course alone may be the most effective action to avoid a close-quarters situation provided that it is made in good time, is substantial and does not result in another close-quarters situation.

(*d*) Action taken to avoid collision with another vessel shall be such as to result in passing at a safe distance. The effectiveness of the action shall be carefully checked until the other vessel is finally past and clear.

(*e*) If necessary to avoid collision or allow more time to assess the situation, a vessel shall slacken her speed or take all way off by stopping or reversing her means of propulsion.

B

RULE 9

Narrow channels

(*a*) A vessel proceeding along the course of a narrow channel or fairway shall keep as near to the outer limit of the channel or fairway which lies on her starboard side as is safe and practicable.

(*b*) A vessel of less than 20 metres in length or a sailing vessel shall not impede the passage of a vessel which can safely navigate only within a narrow channel or fairway.

(*c*) A vessel engaged in fishing shall not impede the passage of any other vessel navigating within a narrow channel or fairway.

(*d*) A vessel shall not cross a narrow channel or fairway if such crossing impedes the passage of a vessel which can safely navigate only within such channel or fairway. The latter vessel may use the sound signal prescribed in Rule 34 (*d*) if in doubt as to the intention of the crossing vessel.

(*e*) (i) In a narrow channel or fairway when overtaking can take place only if the vessel to be overtaken has to take action to permit safe passing, the vessel intending to overtake shall indicate her intention by sounding the appropriate signal prescribed in Rule 34 (*c*) (i). The vessel to be overtaken shall, if in agreement, sound the appropriate signal prescribed in Rule 34 (*c*) (ii) and take steps to permit safe passing. If in doubt she may sound the signals prescribed in Rule 34 (*d*).

(ii) This Rule does not relieve the overtaking vessel of her obligation under Rule 13.

(*f*) A vessel nearing a bend or an area of a narrow channel or fairway where other vessels may be obscured by an intervening obstruction shall navigate with particular alertness and caution and shall sound the appropriate signal prescribed in Rule 34 (*e*).

(g) Any vessel shall, if the circumstances of the case admit, avoid anchoring in a narrow channel.

RULE 10

Traffic separation schemes

(a) This Rule applies to traffic separation schemes adopted by the Organisation:—

(b) A vessel using a traffic separation scheme shall:—

- (i) proceed in the appropriate traffic lane in the general direction of traffic flow for that lane;
- (ii) so far as practicable keep clear of a traffic separation line or separation zone;
- (iii) normally join or leave a traffic lane at the termination of the lane, but when joining or leaving from the side shall do so at as small an angle to the general direction of traffic flow as practicable.

(c) A vessel shall so far as practicable avoid crossing traffic lanes, but if obliged to do so shall cross as nearly as practicable at right angles to the general direction of traffic flow.

(d) Inshore traffic zones shall not normally be used by through traffic which can safely use the appropriate traffic lane within the adjacent traffic separation scheme.

(e) A vessel, other than a crossing vessel, shall not normally enter a separation zone or cross a separation line except:—

- (i) in cases of emergency to avoid immediate danger;
- (ii) to engage in fishing within a separation zone.

(f) A vessel navigating in areas near the terminations of traffic separation schemes shall do so with particular caution.

(*g*) A vessel shall so far as practicable avoid anchoring in a traffic separation scheme or in areas near its terminations.

(*h*) A vessel not using a traffic separation scheme shall avoid it by as wide a margin as is practicable.

(*i*) A vessel engaged in fishing shall not impede the passage of any vessel following a traffic lane.

(*j*) A vessel of less than 20 metres in length or a sailing vessel shall not impede the safe passage of a power-driven vessel following a traffic lane.

Section II.   Conduct of vessels in sight of one another

RULE 11

Application

Rules in this Section apply to vessels in sight of one another.

RULE 12

Sailing vessels

(*a*) When two sailing vessels are approaching one another, so as to involve risk of collision, one of them shall keep out of the way of the other as follows:—

  (i) when each has the wind on a different side, the vessel which has the wind on the port side shall keep out of the way of the other;

  (ii) when both have the wind on the same side, the vessel which is to windward shall keep out of the way of the vessel which is to leeward;

(iii) if a vessel with the wind on the port side sees a vessel to windward and cannot determine with certainty whether the other vessel has the wind on the port or on the starboard side, she shall keep out of the way of the other.

(*b*) For the purposes of this Rule the windward side shall be deemed to be the side opposite to that on which the mainsail is carried or, in the case of a square-rigged vessel, the side opposite to that on which the largest fore-and-aft sail is carried.

RULE 13

Overtaking

(*a*) Notwithstanding anything contained in the Rules of this Section any vessel overtaking any other shall keep out of the way of the vessel being overtaken.

(*b*) A vessel shall be deemed to be overtaking when coming up with another vessel from a direction more than 22·5° abaft her beam, that is, in such a position with reference to the vessel she is overtaking, that at night she would be able to see only the sternlight of that vessel but neither of her sidelights.

(*c*) When a vessel is in doubt as to whether she is overtaking another, she shall assume that this is the case and act accordingly.

(*d*) Any subsequent alteration of the bearing between the two vessels shall not make the overtaking vessel a crossing vessel within the meaning of these Rules or relieve her of the duty of keeping clear of the overtaken vessel until she is finally past and clear.

Rule 14

Head-on situation

(*a*) When two power-driven vessels are meeting on reciprocal or nearly reciprocal courses so as to involve risk of collision each shall alter her course to starboard so that each shall pass on the port side of the other.

(*b*) Such a situation shall be deemed to exist when a vessel sees the other ahead or nearly ahead and by night she could see the masthead lights of the other in a line or nearly in a line and/or both sidelights and by day she observes the corresponding aspect of the other vessel.

(*c*) When a vessel is in any doubt as to whether such a situation exists she shall assume that it does exist and act accordingly.

Rule 15

Crossing situation

When two power-driven vessels are crossing so as to involve risk of collision, the vessel which has the other on her own starboard side shall keep out of the way and shall, if the circumstances of the case admit, avoid crossing ahead of the other vessel.

Rule 16

Action by give-way vessel

Every vessel which is directed to keep out of the way of another vessel shall, so far as possible, take early and substantial action to keep well clear.

RULE 17

Action by stand-on vessel

(*a*) (i) Where one of two vessels is to keep out of the way the other shall keep her course and speed.

(ii) The latter vessel may however take action to avoid collision by her manoeuvre alone, as soon as it becomes apparent to her that the vessel required to keep out of the way is not taking appropriate action in compliance with these Rules.

(*b*) When, from any cause, the vessel required to keep her course and speed finds herself so close that collision cannot be avoided by the action of the give-way vessel alone, she shall take such action as will best aid to avoid collision.

(*c*) A power-driven vessel which takes action in a crossing situation in accordance with sub-paragraph (*a*) (ii) of this Rule to avoid collision with another power-driven vessel shall, if the circumstances of the case admit, not alter course to port for a vessel on her own port side.

(*d*) This Rule does not relieve the give-way vessel of her obligation to keep out of the way.

RULE 18

Responsibilities between vessels

Except where Rules 9, 10 and 13 otherwise require:—

(*a*) A power-driven vessel underway shall keep out of the way of:—

  (i) a vessel not under command;
  (ii) a vessel restricted in her ability to manoeuvre;
  (iii) a vessel engaged in fishing;
  (iv) a sailing vessel.

(*b*) A sailing vessel underway shall keep out of the way of:—

    (i) a vessel not under command;

    (ii) a vessel restricted in her ability to manoeuvre;

    (iii) a vessel engaged in fishing.

(*c*) A vessel engaged in fishing when underway shall, so far as possible, keep out of the way of:—

    (i) a vessel not under command;

    (ii) a vessel restricted in her ability to manoeuvre.

(*d*) (i) Any vessel other than a vessel not under command or a vessel restricted in her ability to manoeuvre shall, if the circumstances of the case admit, avoid impending the safe passage of a vessel constrained by her draught, exhibiting the signals in Rule 28.

    (ii) A vessel constrained by her draught shall navigate with particular caution having full regard to her special condition.

(*e*) A seaplane on the water shall, in general, keep well clear of all vessels and avoid impeding their navigation. In circumstances, however, where risk of collision exists, she shall comply with the Rules of this Part.

Section III.   Conduct of vessels in restricted visibility

RULE 19

Conduct of vessels in restricted visibility

(*a*) This Rule applies to vessels not in sight of one another when navigating in or near an area of restricted visibility.

(*b*) Every vessel shall proceed at a safe speed adapted to the prevailing circumstances and conditions of restricted visibility.

A power-driven vessel shall have her engines ready for immediate manoeuvre.

(c) Every vessel shall have due regard to the prevailing circumstances and conditions of restricted visibility when complying with the Rules of Section I of this Part.

(d) A vessel which detects by radar alone the presence of another vessel shall determine if a close-quarters situation is developing and/or risk of collision exists. If so, she shall take avoiding action in ample time, provided that when such action consists of an alteration of course, so far as possible the following shall be avoided:—

   (i) an alteration of course to port for a vessel forward of the beam, other than for a vessel being overtaken;
   (ii) an alteration of course towards a vessel abeam or abaft the beam.

(e) Except where it has been determined that a risk of collision does not exist, every vessel which hears apparently forward of her beam the fog signal of another vessel, or which cannot avoid a close-quarters situation with another vessel forward of her beam, shall reduce her speed to the minimum at which she can be kept on her course. She shall if necessary take all her way off and in any event navigate with extreme caution until danger of collision is over.

PART C. LIGHTS AND SHAPES

RULE 20

Application

(a) Rules in this Part shall be complied with in all weathers.

(b) The Rules concerning lights shall be complied with

from sunset to sunrise, and during such times no other lights shall be exhibited, except such lights as cannot be mistaken for the lights specified in these Rules or do not impair their visibility or distinctive character, or interfere with the keeping of a proper look-out.

(c) The lights prescribed by these Rules shall, if carried, also be exhibited from sunrise to sunset in restricted visibility and may be exhibited in all other circumstances when it is deemed necessary.

(d) The Rules concerning shapes shall be complied with by day.

(e) The lights and shapes specified in these Rules shall comply with the provisions of Annex I to these Regulations.

RULE 21

Definitions

(a) 'Masthead light' means a white light placed over the fore and aft centreline of the vessel showing an unbroken light over an arc of the horizon of 225° and so fixed as to show the light from right ahead to 22·5° abaft the beam on either side of the vessel.

(b) 'Sidelights' means a green light on the starboard side and a red light on the port side each showing an unbroken light over an arc of the horizon of 112·5° and so fixed as to show the light from right ahead to 22·5° abaft the beam on its respective side. In a vessel of less than 20 metres in length the sidelights may be combined in one lantern carried on the fore and aft centreline of the vessel.

(c) 'Sternlight' means a white light placed as nearly as practicable at the stern showing an unbroken light over an arc of the horizon of 135° and so fixed as to show the light 67·5° from right aft on each side of the vessel.

(d) 'Towing light' means a yellow light having the same characteristics as the 'sternlight' defined in paragraph (c) of this Rule.

(e) 'All round light' means a light showing an unbroken light over an arc of the horizon of 360°.

(f) 'Flashing light' means a light flashing at regular intervals at a frequency of 120 flashes or more per minute.

RULE 22

Visibility of lights

The lights prescribed in these Rules shall have an intensity as specified in Section 8 of Annex I to these Regulations so as to be visible at the following minimum ranges:—

(a) In vessels of 50 metres or more in length:—

—a masthead light, 6 miles;
—a sidelight, 3 miles;
—a sternlight, 3 miles;
—a towing light, 3 miles;
—a white, red, green or yellow all-round light, 3 miles.

(b) In vessels of 12 metres or more in length but less than 50 metres in length:—

—a masthead light, 5 miles; except that where the length of the vessel is less than 20 metres, 3 miles;
—a sidelight, 2 miles;
—a sternlight, 2 miles;
—a towing light, 2 miles;
—a white, red, green or yellow all-round light, 2 miles.

(*c*) In vessels of less than 12 metres in length:—
—a masthead light, 2 miles;
—a sidelight, 1 mile;
—a sternlight, 2 miles;
—a towing light, 2 miles;
—a white, red, green or yellow all-round light, 2 miles.

Rule 23

Power-driven vessels underway

(*a*) A power-driven vessel underway shall exhibit:—
(i) a masthead light forward;
(ii) a second masthead light abaft of and higher than the forward one; except that a vessel of less than 50 metres in length shall not be obliged to exhibit such light but may do so;
(iii) sidelights;
(iv) a sternlight.

(*b*) An air-cushion vessel when operating in the non-displacement mode shall, in addition to the lights prescribed in paragraph (*a*) of this Rule, exhibit an all-round flashing yellow light.

(*c*) A power-driven vessel of less than 7 metres in length and whose maximum speed does not exceed 7 knots may, in lieu of the lights prescribed in paragraph (*a*) of this Rule, exhibit an all-round white light. Such vessel shall, if practicable, also exhibit sidelights.

Rule 24

Towing and pushing

(*a*) A power-driven vessel when towing shall exhibit:—

(i) instead of the light prescribed in Rule 23 (*a*) (i), two masthead lights forward in a vertical line. When the length of the tow, measuring from the stern of the towing vessel to the after end of the tow exceeds 200 metres, three such lights in a vertical line;

(ii) sidelights;

(iii) a sternlight;

(iv) a towing light in a vertical line above the sternlight;

(v) when the length of the tow exceeds 200 metres, a diamond shape where it can best be seen.

(*b*) When a pushing vessel and a vessel being pushed ahead are rigidly connected in a composite unit they shall be regarded as a power-driven vessel and exhibit the lights prescribed in Rule 23.

(*c*) A power-driven vessel when pushing ahead or towing alongside, except in the case of a composite unit, shall exhibit:

(i) instead of the light prescribed in Rule 23 (*a*) (i), two masthead lights forward in a vertical line;

(ii) sidelights;

(iii) a sternlight.

(*d*) A power-driven vessel to which paragraphs (*a*) and (*c*) of this Rule apply shall also comply with Rule 23 (*a*) (ii).

(*e*) A vessel or object being towed shall exhibit:—

(i) sidelights;

(ii) a sternlight;

(iii) when the length of the tow exceeds 200 metres, a diamond shape where it can best be seen.

(*f*) Provided that any number of vessels being towed alongside or pushed in a group shall be lighted as one vessel,

(i) a vessel being pushed ahead, not being part of a composite unit, shall exhibit at the forward end, sidelights;

(ii) a vessel being towed alongside shall exhibit a sternlight and at the forward end, sidelights.

(g) Where from any sufficient cause it is impracticable for a vessel or object being towed to exhibit the lights prescribed in paragraph (e) of this Rule, all possible measures shall be taken to light the vessel or object towed or at least to indicate the presence of the unlighted vessel or object.

RULE 25

Sailing vessels underway and vessels under oars

(a) A sailing vessel underway shall exhibit:—
  (i) sidelights;
  (ii) a sternlight.

(b) In a sailing vessel of less than 12 metres in length the lights prescribed in paragraph (a) of this Rule may be combined in one lantern carried at or near the top of the mast where it can best be seen.

(c) A sailing vessel underway may, in addition to the lights prescribed in paragraph (a) of this Rule, exhibit at or near the top of the mast, where they can best be seen, two all-round lights in a vertical line, the upper being red and the lower green, but these lights shall not be exhibited in conjunction with the combined lantern permitted by paragraph (b) of this Rule.

(d) (i) A sailing vessel of less than 7 metres in length shall, if practicable, exhibit the lights prescribed in paragraph (a) or (b) of this Rule, but if she does not, she shall have ready at hand an electric torch or lighted lantern showing a white light which shall be exhibited in sufficient time to prevent collision.

  (ii) A vessel under oars may exhibit the lights prescribed in this Rule for sailing vessels, but if she does not, she shall have ready at hand an electric torch or lighted lantern showing a white light which shall be exhibited in sufficient time to prevent collision.

(e) A vessel proceeding under sail when also being propelled by machinery shall exhibit forward where it can best be seen a conical shape, apex downwards.

RULE 26

Fishing vessels

(a) A vessel engaged in fishing, whether underway or at anchor, shall exhibit only the lights and shapes prescribed in this Rule.

(b) A vessel when engaged in trawling, by which is meant the dragging through the water of a dredge net or other apparatus used as a fishing appliance, shall exhibit:—

  (i) two all-round lights in a vertical line, the upper being green and the lower white, or a shape consisting of two cones with their apexes together in a vertical line, one above the other; a vessel of less than 20 metres in length may instead of this shape exhibit a basket;

 (ii) a masthead light abaft of and higher than the all-round green light; a vessel of less than 50 metres in length shall not be obliged to exhibit such a light but may do so;

(iii) when making way through the water, in addition to the lights prescribed in this paragraph, sidelights and a sternlight.

(c) A vessel engaged in fishing, other than trawling, shall exhibit:—

  (i) two all-round lights in a vertical line, the upper being red and the lower white, or a shape consisting of two cones with apexes together in a vertical line, one above the other; a vessel of less than 20 metres in length may instead of this shape exhibit a basket;

(ii) when there is outlying gear extending more than 150 metres horizontally from the vessel, an all-round white light or a cone apex upwards in the direction of the gear;

(iii) when making way through the water, in addition to the lights prescribed in this paragraph, sidelights and a sternlight.

(d) A vessel engaged in fishing in close proximity to other vessels engaged in fishing may exhibit the additional signals described in Annex II to these Regulations.

(e) A vessel when not engaged in fishing shall not exhibit the lights or shapes prescribed in this Rule, but only those prescribed for a vessel of her length.

RULE 27

Vessels not under command or restricted in their ability to manoeuvre

(a) A vessel not under command shall exhibit:—

(i) two all-round red lights in a vertical line where they can best be seen;

(ii) two balls or similar shapes in a vertical line where they can best be seen;

(iii) when making way through the water, in addition to the lights prescribed in this paragraph, sidelights and a sternlight.

(b) A vessel restricted in her ability to manoeuvre, except a vessel engaged in minesweeping operations, shall exhibit:—

(i) three all-round lights in a vertical line where they can best be seen. The highest and lowest of these lights shall be red and the middle light shall be white;

(ii) three shapes in a vertical line where they can best be seen. The highest and lowest of these shapes shall be balls and the middle one a diamond;

(iii) when making way through the water, masthead lights, sidelights and a sternlight, in addition to the lights prescribed in sub-paragraph (i);

(iv) when at anchor, in addition to the lights or shapes prescribed in sub-paragraphs (i) and (ii), the light, lights or shape prescribed in Rule 30.

(c) A vessel engaged in a towing operation such as renders her unable to deviate from her course shall, in addition to the lights or shapes prescribed in sub-paragraph (b) (i) and (ii) of this Rule, exhibit the lights or shape prescribed in Rule 24 (a).

(d) A vessel engaged in dredging or underwater operations when restricted in her ability to manoeuver, shall exhibit the lights and shapes prescribed in paragraph (b) of this Rule and shall in addition, when obstruction exists, exhibit:—

(i) two all-round red lights or two balls in a vertical line to indicate the side on which the obstruction exists;

(ii) two all-round green lights or two diamonds in a vertical line to indicate the side on which another vessel may pass;

(iii) when making way through the water, in addition to the lights prescribed in this paragraph, masthead lights, sidelights and a sternlight;

(iv) a vessel to which this paragraph applies when at anchor shall exhibit the lights or shapes prescribed in sub-paragraphs (i) and (ii) instead of the lights or shape prescribed in Rule 30.

C

(*e*) Whenever the size of a vessel engaged in diving operations makes it impracticable to exhibit the shapes prescribed in paragraph (*d*) of this Rule, a rigid replica of the International Code flag 'A' not less than 1 metre in height shall be exhibited. Measures shall be taken to ensure all-round visibility.

(*f*) A vessel engaged in minesweeping operations shall, in addition to the lights prescribed for a power-driven vessel in Rule 23, exhibit three all-round green lights or three balls. One of these lights or shapes shall be exhibited at or near the foremast head and one at each end of the fore yard. These lights or shapes indicate that it is dangerous for another vessel to approach closer than 1,000 metres astern or 500 metres on either side of the minesweeper.

(*g*) Vessels of less than 7 metres in length shall not be required to exhibit the lights prescribed in this Rule.

(*h*) The signals prescribed in this Rule are not signals of vessels in distress and requiring assistance. Such signals are contained in Annex IV to these Regulations.

RULE 28

Vessels constrained by their draught

A vessel constrained by her draught may, in addition to the lights prescribed for power-driven vessels in Rule 23, exhibit where they can best be seen three all-round red lights in a vertical line, or a cylinder.

RULE 29

Pilot vessels

(*a*) A vessel engaged on pilotage duty shall exhibit:—

  (i) at or near the masthead, two all-round lights in a
      vertical line, the upper being white and the lower red;
 (ii) when underway, in addition, sidelights and a stern-
      light;
(iii) when at anchor, in addition to the lights prescribed in
      sub-paragraph (i), the anchor light, lights or shape.

(*b*) A pilot vessel when not engaged on pilotage duty shall
exhibit the lights or shapes prescribed for a similar vessel of
her length.

RULE 30

Anchored vessels and vessels aground

(*a*) A vessel at anchor shall exhibit where it can best be
seen:—

  (i) in the fore part, an all-round white light or one ball;
 (ii) at or near the stern and at a lower level than the light
      prescribed in sub-paragraph (i), an all-round white
      light.

(*b*) A vessel of less than 50 metres in length may exhibit an
all-round white light where it can best be seen instead of the
lights prescribed in paragraph (*a*) of this Rule.

(*c*) A vessel at anchor may, and a vessel of 100 metres and
more in length shall, also use the available working or equivalent lights to illuminate her decks.

(*d*) A vessel aground shall exhibit the lights prescribed in
paragraph (*a*) or (*b*) of this Rule and in addition, where they
can best be seen:—

  (i) two all-round red lights in a vertical line;
 (ii) three balls in a vertical line.

(*e*) A vessel of less than 7 metres in length, when at anchor
or aground, not in or near a narrow channel, fairway or

anchorage, or where other vessels normally navigate, shall not be required to exhibit the lights or shapes prescribed in paragraphs (*a*), (*b*) or (*d*) of this Rule.

RULE 31

Seaplanes

Where it is impracticable for a seaplane to exhibit lights and shapes of the characteristics or in the positions prescribed in the Rules of this Part she shall exhibit lights and shapes as closely similar in characteristics and position as is possible.

PART D.   SOUND AND LIGHT SIGNALS

RULE 32

Definitions

(*a*) The word 'whistle' means any sound signalling appliance capable of producing the prescribed blasts and which complies with the specifications in Annex III to these Regulations.

(*b*) The term 'short blast' means a blast of about one second's duration.

(*c*) The term 'prolonged blast' means a blast of from four to six seconds' duration.

RULE 33

Equipment for sound signals

(*a*) A vessel of 12 metres or more in length shall be provided with a whistle and a bell and a vessel of 100 metres or more in length shall, in addition, be provided with a gong, the tone and sound of which cannot be confused with that of the bell. The whistle, bell and gong shall comply with the specifications in Annex III to these Regulations. The bell or gong or both may be replaced by other equipment having the same respective sound characteristics provided that manual sounding of the required signals shall always be possible.

(*b*) A vessel of less than 12 metres in length shall not be obliged to carry the sound signalling appliances prescribed in paragraph (*a*) of this Rule but if she does not, she shall be provided with some other means of making an efficient sound signal.

Rule 34

Manoeuvring and warning signals

(*a*) When vessels are in sight of one another, a power-driven vessel underway, when manoeuvring as authorised or required by these Rules, shall indicate that manoeuvre by the following signals on her whistle:—

—one short blast to mean 'I am altering my course to starboard';

—two short blasts to mean 'I am altering my course to port';

—three short blasts to mean 'I am operating astern propulsion'.

(*b*) Any vessel may supplement the whistle signals prescribed in paragraph (*a*) of this Rule by light signals, repeated as appropriate, whilst the manoeuvre is being carried out:—

(i) these light signals shall have the following significance:—

—one flash to mean 'I am altering my course to starboard';

—two flashes to mean 'I am altering my course to port';

—three flashes to mean 'I am operating astern propulsion';

(ii) the duration of each flash shall be about one second, the interval between flashes shall be about one second, and the interval between successive signals shall be not less than ten seconds;

(iii) the light used for this signal shall, if fitted, be an all-round white light, visible at a minimum range of 5 miles, and shall comply with the provisions of Annex I.

(c) When in sight of one another in a narrow channel or fairway:—

(i) a vessel intending to overtake another shall in compliance with Rule 9 (e) (i) indicate her intention by the following signals on her whistle:—

—two prolonged blasts followed by one short blast to mean 'I intend to overtake you on your starboard side';

—two prolonged blasts followed by two short blasts to mean 'I intend to overtake you on your port side'.

(ii) the vessel about to be overtaken when acting in accordance with Rule 9 (e) (i) shall indicate her agreement by the following signal on her whistle:—

—one prolonged, one short, one prolonged and one short blast, in that order.

(d) When vessels in sight of one another are approaching each other and from any cause either vessel fails to understand the intentions or actions of the other, or is in doubt whether sufficient action is being taken by the other to avoid collision, the vessel in doubt shall immediately indicate such doubt by giving at least five short and rapid blasts on the whistle. Such signal may be supplemented by a light signal of at least five short and rapid flashes.

(e) A vessel nearing a bend or an area of a channel or fairway where other vessels may be obscured by an intervening obstruction shall sound one prolonged blast. Such signal shall be answered with a prolonged blast by any approaching vessel that may be within hearing around the bend or behind the intervening obstruction.

(f) If whistles are fitted on a vessel at a distance apart of more than 100 metres, one whistle only shall be used for giving manoeuvring and warning signals.

RULE 35

Sound signals in restricted visibility

In or near an area of restricted visibility, whether by day or night, the signals prescribed in this Rule shall be used as follows:—

(a) A power-driven vessel making way through the water shall sound at intervals of not more than 2 minutes one prolonged blast.

(b) A power-driven vessel underway but stopped and making no way through the water shall sound at intervals of not more than 2 minutes two prolonged blasts in succession with an interval of about 2 seconds between them.

(c) A vessel not under command, a vessel restricted in her ability to manoeuvre, a vessel constrained by her draught, a sailing vessel, a vessel engaged in fishing and a vessel engaged in towing or pushing another vessel shall, instead of the signals prescribed in paragraphs (*a*) or (*b*) of this Rule, sound at intervals of not more than 2 minutes three blasts in succession, namely one prolonged followed by two short blasts.

(*d*) A vessel towed or if more than one vessel is towed the last vessel of the tow, if manned, shall at intervals of not more than 2 minutes sound four blasts in succession, namely one prolonged followed by three short blasts. When practicable, this signal shall be made immediately after the signal made by the towing vessel.

(*e*) When a pushing vessel and a vessel being pushed ahead are rigidly connected in a composite unit they shall be regarded as a power-driven vessel and shall give the signals prescribed in paragraphs (*a*) or (*b*) of this Rule.

(*f*) A vessel at anchor shall at intervals of not more than one minute ring the bell rapidly for about 5 seconds. In a vessel of 100 metres or more in length the bell shall be sounded in the forepart of the vessel and immediately after the ringing of the bell the gong shall be sounded rapidly for about 5 seconds in the after part of the vessel. A vessel at anchor may in addition sound three blasts in succession, namely one short, one prolonged and one short blast, to give warning of her position and of the possibility of collision to an approaching vessel.

(*g*) A vessel aground shall give the bell signal and if required the gong signal prescribed in paragraph (*f*) of this Rule and shall, in addition, give three separate and distinct strokes on the bell immediately before and after the rapid ringing of the bell. A vessel aground may in addition sound an appropriate whistle signal.

(h) A vessel of less than 12 metres in length shall not be obliged to give the above-mentioned signals but, if she does not, shall make some other efficient sound signal at intervals of not more than 2 minutes.

(i) A pilot vessel when engaged on pilotage duty may in addition to the signals prescribed in paragraphs (a), (b) or (f) of this Rule sound an identity signal consisting of four short blasts.

RULE 36

Signals to attract attention

If necessary to attract the attention of another vessel any vessel may make light or sound signals that cannot be mistaken for any signal authorised elsewhere in these Rules, or may direct the beam of her searchlight in the direction of the danger, in such a way as not to embarrass any vessel.

RULE 37

Distress signals

When a vessel is in distress and requires assistance she shall use or exhibit the signals prescribed in Annex IV to these Regulations.

PART E.   EXEMPTIONS

RULE 38

Exemptions

Any vessel (or class of vessels) provided that she complies

with the requirements of the International Regulations for Preventing Collisions at Sea, 1960, the keel of which is laid or which is at a corresponding stage of construction before the entry into force of these Regulations may be exempted from compliance therewith as follows:—

(*a*) The installation of lights with ranges prescribed in Rule 22, until four years after the date of entry into force of these Regulations.

(*b*) The installation of lights with colour specifications as prescribed in Section 7 of Annex I to these Regulations, until four years after the date of entry into force of these Regulations.

(*c*) The repositioning of lights as a result of conversion from Imperial to metric units and rounding off measurement figures, permanent exemption.

(*d*) (i) The repositioning of masthead lights on vessels of less than 150 metres in length, resulting from the prescriptions of Section 3 (*a*) of Annex I, permanent exemption.

(ii) The repositioning of masthead lights on vessels of 150 metres or more in length, resulting from the prescriptions of Section 3 (*a*) of Annex I to these Regulations, until nine years after the date of entry into force of these Regulations.

(*e*) The repositioning of masthead lights resulting from the prescriptions of Section 2 (*b*) of Annex I, until nine years after the date of entry into force of these Regulations.

(*f*) The repositioning of sidelights resulting from the prescriptions of Sections 2 (*g*) and 3 (*b*) of Annex I, until nine years after the date of entry into force of these Regulations.

(g) The requirements for sound signal appliances prescribed in Annex III, until nine years after the date of entry into force of these Regulations.

ANNEX I

Positioning and technical details of lights and shapes

1. *Definition*

The term 'height above the hull' means height above the uppermost continuous deck.

2. *Vertical positioning and spacing of lights*

(a) On a power-driven vessel of 20 metres or more in length the masthead lights shall be placed as follows:—

    (i) the forward masthead light, or if only one masthead light is carried, then that light, at a height above the hull of not less than 6 metres, and, if the breadth of the vessel exceeds 6 metres, then at a height above the hull not less than such breadth, so however that the light need not be placed at a greater height above the hull than 12 metres;

    (ii) when two masthead lights are carried the after one shall be at least 4·5 metres vertically higher than the forward one.

(b) The vertical separation of masthead lights of power-driven vessels shall be such that in all normal conditions of trim after light will be seen over and separate from the forward light at a distance of 1000 metres from the stem when viewed from sea level.

(*c*) The masthead light of a power-driven vessel of 12 metres but less than 20 metres in length shall be placed at a height above the gunwale of not less than 2·5 metres.

(*d*) A power-driven vessel of less than 12 metres in length may carry the uppermost light at a height of less than 2·5 metres above the gunwale. When however a masthead light is carried in addition to sidelights and a sternlight, then such masthead light shall be carried at least 1 metre higher than the sidelights.

(*e*) One of the two or three masthead lights prescribed for a power-driven vessel when engaged in towing or pushing another vessel shall be placed in the same position as the forward masthead light of a power-driven vessel.

(*f*) In all circumstances the masthead light or lights shall be so placed as to be above and clear of all other lights and obstructions.

(*g*) The sidelights of a power-driven vessel shall be placed at a height above the hull not greater than three-quarters of that of the forward masthead light. They shall not be so low as to be interfered with by deck lights.

(*h*) The sidelights, if in a combined lantern and carried on a power-driven vessel of less than 20 metres in length, shall be placed not less than 1 metre below the masthead light.

(*i*) When the Rules prescribe two or three lights to be carried in a vertical line, they shall be spaced as follows:—

    (i) on a vessel of 20 metres in length or more such lights shall be spaced not less than 2 metres apart, and the lowest of these lights shall, except where a towing light is required, not less than 4 metres above the hull;

    (ii) on a vessel of less than 20 metres in length such lights shall be spaced not less than 1 metre apart and the lowest of these lights shall, except where a towing light is required, not be less than 2 metres above the gunwale;

(iii) when three lights are carried they shall be equally spaced.

(j) The lower of the two all-round lights prescribed for a fishing vessel when engaged in fishing shall be at a height above the sidelights not less than twice the distance between the two vertical lights.

(k) The forward anchor light, when two are carried, shall not be less than 4·5 metres above the after one. On a vessel of 50 metres or more in length this forward anchor light shall not be less than 6 metres above the hull.

3. *Horizontal positioning and spacing of lights*

(a) When two masthead lights are prescribed for a power-driven vessel, the horizontal distance between them shall not be less than one-half of the length of the vessel but need not be more than 100 metres. The forward light shall be placed not more than one-quarter of the length of the vessel from the stem.

(b) On a vessel of 20 metres or more in length the sidelights shall not be placed in front of the forward masthead lights. They shall be placed at or near the side of the vessel.

4. *Details of location of direction-indicating lights for fishing vessels, dredgers and vessels engaged in underwater operations*

(a) The light indicating the direction of the outlying gear from a vessel engaged in fishing as prescribed in Rule 26 (c) (ii) shall be placed at a horizontal distance of not less than 2 metres and not more than 6 metres away from the two all-round red and white lights. This light shall be placed not higher than the all-round white light prescribed in Rule 26 (c) (i) and not lower than the sidelights.

(b) The lights and shapes on a vessel engaged in dredging or underwater operations to indicate the obstructed side and/or the side on which it is safe to pass, as prescribed in Rule 27 (d) (i) and (ii), shall be placed at the maximum practical horizontal distance, but in no case less than 2 metres, from the lights or shapes prescribed in Rule 27 (b) (i) and (ii). In no case shall the upper of these lights or shapes be at a greater height than the lower of the three lights or shapes prescribed in Rule 27 (b) (i) and (ii).

5.   Screens for sidelights

The sidelights shall be fitted with inboard screens painted matt black, and meeting the requirements of Section 9 of this Annex. With a combined lantern, using a single vertical filament and a very narrow division between the green and red sections, external screens need not be fitted.

6.   Shapes

(a) Shapes shall be black and of the following sizes:—
   (i) a ball shall have a diameter of not less than 0·6 metre:
  (ii) a cone shall have a base diameter of not less than 0·6 metre and a height equal to its diameter;
 (iii) a cylinder shall have a diameter of at least 0·6 metre and a height of twice its diameter;
 (iv) a diamond shape shall consist of two cones as defined in (ii) above having a common base.

(b) The vertical distance between shapes shall be at least 1·5 metre.

(c) In a vessel of less than 20 metres in length, shapes of

lesser dimensions but commensurate with the size of the vessel may be used and the distance apart may be correspondingly reduced.

7. Colour specification of lights

The chromaticity of all navigation lights shall conform to the following standards, which lie within the boundaries of the area of the diagram specified for each colour by the International Commission on Illumination (CIE).

The boundaries of the area for each colour are given by indicating the corner co-ordinates, which are as follows:—

(i) *White*

x	0·525	0·525	0·452	0·310	0·310	0·443
y	0·382	0·440	0·440	0·348	0·283	0·382

(ii) *Green*

x	0·028	0·009	0·300	0·203
y	0·385	0·723	0·511	0·356

(iii) *Red*

x	0·680	0·660	0·735	0·721
y	0·320	0·320	0·265	0·259

(iv) *Yellow*

x	0·612	0·618	0·575	0·575
y	0·382	0·382	0·425	0·406

8. Intensity of lights

(*a*) The minimum luminous intensity of lights shall be calculated by using the formula:—

$$1 = 3·43 \times 10^6 \times T \times D^2 \times K^{-D}$$

where I   is luminous intensity in candelas under service conditions,

T   is threshold factor 2×10^{-7} lux,

D   is range of visibility (luminous range) of the light in nautical miles,

K   is atmospheric transmissivity.

For prescribed lights the value of K shall be 0·8, corresponding to a meteorological visibility of approximately 13 nautical miles.

(b) A selection of figures derived from the formula is given in the following table:—

Range of visibility (luminous range) of light in nautical miles D	Luminous intensity of light in candelas for K = 0·8 I
1	0·9
2	4·3
3	12
4	27
5	52
6	94

NOTE—The maximum luminous intensity of navigation lights should be limited to avoid undue glare.

9. *Horizontal sectors*

(a) (i) In the forward direction, sidelights as fitted on the vessel must show the minimum required intensities. The intensities must decrease to reach practical cut-off between 1° and 3° outside the prescribed sectors.

(ii) For sternlights and masthead lights and at 22·5° abaft the beam for sidelights, the minimum required intensities shall be maintained over the

arc of the horizon up to 5° within the limits of the
sectors prescribed in Rule 21. From 5° within the
prescribed sectors the intensity may decrease by
50 per cent up to the prescribed limits; it shall
decrease steadily to reach practical cut-off at not
more than 5° outside the prescribed limits.

(*b*) All-round lights shall be so located as not to be
obscured by masts, topmasts or structures within angular
sectors of more than 6°, except anchor lights, which need not
be placed at an impracticable height above the hull.

10.   *Vertical sectors*

(*a*) The vertical sectors of electric lights, with the exception
of lights on sailing vessels shall ensure that:—

   (i) at least the required minimum intensity is maintained
       at all angles from 5° above to 5° below the horizontal;
  (ii) at least 60 per cent of the required minimum intensity
       is maintained from 7·5° above to 7·5° below the
       horizontal.
  (*b*) In the case of sailing vessels the vertical sectors of
       electric lights shall ensure that:—
   (i) at least the required minimum intensity is maintained
       at all angles from 5° above to 5° below the horizontal;
  (ii) at least 50 per cent of the required minimum intensity
       is maintained from 25° above to 25° below the
       horizontal.

(*c*) In the case of lights other than electric these specifications shall be met as closely as possible.

11.   *Intensity of non-electric lights*

Non-electric lights shall so far as practicable comply with
D

the minimum intensities, as specified in the Table given in Section 8 of this Annex.

12. *Manoeuvring light*

Notwithstanding the provisions of paragraph 2 (*f*) of this Annex the manoeuvring light described in Rule 34 (*b*) shall be placed in the same fore and aft vertical plane as the masthead light or lights and, where practicable, at a minimum height of 2 metres vertically above the forward masthead light, provided that it shall be carried not less than 2 metres vertically above or below the after masthead light. On a vessel where only one masthead light is carried, the manoeuvring light, if fitted, shall be carried where it can best be seen, not less than 2 metres vertically apart from the masthead light.

13. *Approval*

The construction of lanterns and shapes and the installation of lanterns on board the vessel shall be to the satisfaction of the appropriate authority of the State where the vessel is registered.

ANNEX II

Additional signals for fishing vessels fishing in close proximity

1. *General*

The lights mentioned herein shall, if exhibited in pursuance of Rule 26 (*d*), be placed where they can best be seen. They shall be at least 0·9 metre apart but at a lower level than lights prescribed in Rule 26 (*b*) (i) and (*c*) (i). The lights shall be visible all round the horizon at a distance of at least 1 mile

but at a lesser distance than the lights prescribed by these
Rules for fishing vessels.

2. *Signals for trawlers*
(*a*) Vessels when engaged in trawling, whether using
demersal or pelagic gear, may exhibit:—
  (i) when shooting their nets:—
      two white lights in a vertical line;
  (ii) when hauling their nets:—
      one white light over one red light in a vertical line;
  (iii) when the net has come fast upon an obstruction:—
      two red lights in a vertical line.

(*b*) Each vessel engaged in pair trawling may exhibit:—
  (i) by night, a searchlight directed forward and in the
      direction of the other vessel of the pair;
  (ii) when shooting or hauling their nets or when their nets
      have come fast upon an obstruction, the lights pre-
      scribed in 2 (*a*) above.

3. *Signals for purse seiners*
Vessels engaged in fishing with purse seine gear may exhibit
two yellow lights in a vertical line. These lights shall flash
alternately every second and with equal light and occultation
duration. These lights may be exhibited only when the vessel
is hampered by its fishing gear.

ANNEX III

Technical details of sound signal appliances

1. *Whistles*
(*a*) *Frequencies and range of audibility*

The fundamental frequency of the signal shall lie within the range 70–700 Hz.

The range of audibility of the signal from a whistle shall be determined by those frequencies, which may include the fundamental and/or one or more higher frequencies, which lie within the range 180–700 Hz ($\pm$ 1 per cent) and which provide the sound pressure levels specified in paragraph 1 (c) below.

(b) *Limits of fundamental frequencies*

To ensure a wide variety of whistle characteristics, the fundamental frequency of a whistle shall be between the following limits:—

(i) 70–200 Hz, for a vessel 200 metres or more in length;

(ii) 130–350 Hz, for a vessel 75 metres but less than 200 metres in length;

(iii) 250–700 Hz, for a vessel less than 75 metres in length.

(c) *Sound signal intensity and range of audibility*

A whistle fitted in a vessel shall provide, in the direction of maximum intensity of the whistle and at a distance of 1 metre from it, a sound pressure level in at least one 1/3rd-octave band within the range of frequencies 180–700 Hz ($\pm$ 1 per cent) of not less than the appropriate figure given in the table below.

Length of vessel in metres	1/3rd-octave band level at 1 metre in dB referred to 2×10^{-5} N/m^2	Audibility range in nautical miles
200 or more ..	143	2
75 but less than 200	138	1·5
20 but less than 75	130	1
Less than 20 ..	120	0·5

The range of audibility in the table above is for information and is approximately the range at which a whistle may be heard on its forward axis with 90 per cent probability in conditions of still air on board a vessel having average background noise level at the listening posts (taken to be 68 dB in the octave band centred on 250 Hz and 63 dB in the octave band centred on 500 Hz).

In practice the range at which a whistle may be heard is extremely variable and depends critically on weather conditions; the values given can be regarded as typical but under conditions of strong wind or high ambient noise level at the listening post the range may be much reduced.

(*d*) *Directional properties*

The sound pressure level of a directional whistle shall be not more than 4 dB below the sound pressure level on the axis at any direction in the horizontal plane within $\pm$ 45° of the axis. The sound pressure level at any other direction in the horizontal plane shall be not more than 10 dB below the sound pressure level on the axis, so that the range in any direction will be at least half the range on the forward axis. The sound pressure level shall be measured in that 1/3rd-octave band which determines the audibility range.

(*e*) *Positioning of whistles*

When a directional whistle is to be used as the only whistle on a vessel, it shall be installed with its maximum intensity directed straight ahead.

A whistle shall be placed as high as practicable on a vessel, in order to reduce interception of the emitted sound by obstructions and also to minimise hearing damage risk to personnel. The sound pressure level of the vessel's own signal at listening posts shall not exceed 110 dB (A) and so far as practicable should not exceed 100 dB (A).

(f) Fitting of more than one whistle

If whistles are fitted at a distance apart of more than 100 metres, it shall be so arranged that they are not sounded simultaneously.

(g) Combined whistle systems

If due to the presence of obstructions the sound field of a single whistle or of one of the whistles referred to in paragraph 1 *(f)* above is likely to have a zone of greatly reduced signal level, it is recommended that a combined whistle system be fitted so as to overcome this reduction. For the purposes of the Rules a combined whistle system is to be regarded as a single whistle. The whistles of a combined system shall be located at a distance apart of not more than 100 metres and arranged to be sounded simultaneously. The frequency of any one whistle shall differ from those of the others by at least 10 Hz.

2.   *Bell or gong*

(a) Intensity of signal

A bell or gong, or other device having similar sound characteristics shall produce a sound pressure level of not less than 110 dB at 1 metre.

(b) Construction

Bells and gongs shall be made of corrosion-resistant material and designed to give a clear tone. The diameter of the mouth of the bell shall be not less than 300 mm. for vessels of more than 20 metres in length, and shall be not less than 200 mm. for vessels of 12 to 20 metres in length. Where practicable, a power-driven bell striker is recommended to ensure constant force but manual operation shall be possible. The mass of the striker shall be not less than 3 per cent of the mass of the bell.

3. *Approval*

The construction of sound signal appliances, their performance and their installation on board the vessel shall be to the satisfaction of the appropriate authority of the State where the vessel is registered.

ANNEX IV

Distress signals

1. The following signals, used or exhibited either together or separately, indicates distress and need of assistance:—

(*a*) a gun or other explosive signal fired at intervals of about a minute;

(*b*) a continuous sounding with any fog-signalling apparatus;

(*c*) rockets or shells, throwing red stars fired one at a time at short intervals;

(*d*) a signal made by radiotelegraphy or by any other signalling method consisting of the group . . . — — — · · · (SOS) in the Morse Code;

(*e*) a signal sent by radiotelephony consisting of the spoken word 'Mayday';

(*f*) the International Code Signal of distress indicated by N.C.;

(*g*) a signal consisting of a square flag having above or below it a ball or anything resembling a ball;

(*h*) flames on the vessel (as from a burning tar barrel, oil barrel, etc.);

(*i*) a rocket parachute flare or a hand flare showing a red light;

(*j*) a smoke signal giving off orange-coloured smoke;

(*k*) slowly and repeatedly raising and lowering arms outstretched to each side;

(*l*) the radiotelegraph alarm signal;

(*m*) the radiotelephone alarm signal;

(*n*) signals transmitted by emergency position-indicating radio beacons.

2.   The use or exhibition of any of the foregoing signals except for the purpose of indicating distress and need of assistance and the use of other signals which may be confused with any of the above signals is prohibited.

3.   Attention is drawn to the relevant sections of the International Code of Signals, the Merchant Ship Search and Rescue Manual and the following signals:—

(*a*) a piece of orange-coloured canvas with either a black square and circle or other appropriate symbol (for identification from the air);

(*b*) a dye marker.

TABLE SHOWING COLOUR AND RANGE OF LIGHTS CARRIED BY DIFFERENT TYPES OF VESSELS

Power-driven Vessels
(Underway and 50 or more metres in length)

Rule	Type of Light	Colour	Range Miles
22 (a) & 23	Masthead lights	White	6
22 (a) & 23	Side light	Green	3
22 (a) & 23	Side light	Red	3
22 (a) & 23	Stern light	White	3
22 (b)	Masthead light (50 to 20 metres)	White	5
22 (b)	Masthead light (20 to 12 metres)	White	3
22 (c)	Masthead light (less than 12 metres)	White	2
22 (b)	Side light (50 to 12 metres)	Green	2
22 (b)	Side light (50 to 12 metres)	Red	2
22 (b)	Stern light (50 to 12 metres)	White	2
22 (c)	Stern light (less than 12 metres)	White	2
22 (c)	Side light (less than 12 metres)	Green	1
22 (c)	Side light (less than 12 metres)	Red	1
23	All round light (less than 7 metres Maximum speed 7 knots)	White	—
23	Side lights if practicable	Green & Red	—

Air-cushion Vessel in the non-displacement mode

Rule	Type of Light	Colour	Range Miles
23 (a), (b)	All round flashing light (50 metres or more)	Yellow	3
23 (a), (b)	All round flashing light (less than 50 metres)	Yellow	2
23 (a), (b)	Also Masthead, Side & Stern lights	(As classed above)	

Vessels Towing

Rule	Type of Light	Colour	Range Miles
22	Two Masthead lights forward	White	6 to 2
23	(Tow less than 200 metres)	White	

Rule	Type of Light	Colour	Range Miles
24	Three Masthead lights forward (Tow exceeding (200 metres)	White White	6 to 2
	Second Masthead light abaft and higher. (Optional for tugs below 50 metres length)	White	6 to 2
	Side light	Green	3 to 2
	Side light	Red	3 to 2
	Stern light	White	3 to 2
	Towing light above the stern light	Yellow	3 to 2
27 (c)	Three All round lights in vertical line. (Tug unable to manoeuvre)	Red White Red	3 to 2

Vessel being Towed

Rule	Type of Light	Colour	Range Miles
24 (c) (f)	Side light	Green	3 or 2
	Side light	Red	3 or 2
	Stern light	White	3 or 2
	Several vessels Towed alongside or being Pushed ahead are considered a group to be lighted as one vessel		

Pushing Vessel Rigidly Connected to Vessel Pushed Ahead

Rule	Type of Light	Colour	Range Miles
24 (b)	This composite unit is regarded as a power-driven vessel and exhibits the lights prescribed in Rule 23		

Sailing Vessels Underway

Rule	Type of Light	Colour	Range Miles
25 and 22	Side light	Green	3, 2 or 1
	Side light	Red	3, 2 or 1

Rule	Type of Light	Colour	Range Miles
25	Side light under 12 metres. Combined lantern carried near masthead	Red & Green	
25	Stern light	White	3 or 2
25	Optional except with combined lantern. All round masthead lights	Red above Green	
25	Under 7 metres all round	White	

Fishing Vessels

Rule	Type of Light	Colour	Range Miles
26, 22	*Trawlers* only. All round lights in vertical line	Green White	3 or 2 3 or 2
	Masthead light abaft of and higher than the green light	White	6, 5 or
	Side lights when making way	Green & Red	3 or 2
	Stern light when making way	White	3 or 2
26, 22	*Fishing*, other than Trawling	Red	3 or 2
	All round lights in vertical line	White	
	All round light in direction of gear extending horizontally 150 metres	White	3 or 2
	Side lights when making way	Green & Red	3 or 2
	Stern light when making way	White	3 or 2
Annex II	Trawlers may exhibit:—		
	Two all round lights in vertical line	White	
	When shooting nets	White	1
	Two all round lights in vertical line when hauling nets	White Red	1
	Two all round lights in vertical line when nets become obstructed	Red Red	1
	Pair Trawlers may each exhibit:—		
	A searchlight directed forward of the other in addition to lights for trawlers		

Vessel Not Under Command

Rule	Type of Light	Colour	Range Miles
27 (*a*), 22	All round lights in vertical line	Red	3 or 2
	When making way exhibits in addition Side lights and a stern light	Red	

Vessels Restricted in Ability to Manoeuvre

Rule	Type of Light	Colour	Range Miles
27 (*b*)	Three all round lights in vertical line	Red White Red	3 or 2
	When making way exhibits in addition:—		
	Masthead lights Side lights Stern light		

Dredging or Underwater Operations

Rule	Type of Light	Colour	Range Miles
27 (*b*)	In addition to the lights required	Red	
27 (*d*)	27 (*b*). Two all round lights in vertical line. (Obstruction exists on this side.)	Red	3 or 2
	Two all round lights in vertical line (Clear to pass on this side)	Green Green	3 or 2
	When making way exhibits in addition:—		
23	Masthead lights Side lights Stern light		
	When at anchor exhibits the special lights required above. Rule 30 does not apply		

Vessels Minesweeping

Rule	Type of Light	Colour	Range Miles
	In addition to the lights for power-driven vessel:—		

Rule	Type of Light	Colour	Range Miles
27 (d)	Three all round lights (one near the foremast head and one at each end of the fore-yard)	Green	3 or 2

Vessels Constrained by their Draught

Rule	Type of Light	Colour	Range Miles
28	Three all round lights in vertical line	Red	
23	In addition to the lights for a	Red	3 or 2
22	power-driven vessel	Red	

Pilot Vessel

Rule	Type of Light	Colour	Range Miles
29 (a)	Two all round lights in vertical line and in addition when underway:—	White	3 or 2
22	Side lights and a Stern light	Red	
	Or when at anchor:— Anchor light or lights		

Anchored Vessels

Rule	Type of Light	Colour	Range Miles
30 (a)	All round light in the forepart	White	3 or 2
22	All round light at or near the stern	White	3 or 2
30 (b)	A vessel of less than 50 metres may exhibit one all round light	White	2

Vessel Aground

Rule	Type of Light	Colour	Range Miles
30 (d)	Two all round lights in vertical line in addition to the Anchor lights	Red Red	3 or 2

SUMMARY OF SOUND SIGNALS

The word 'whistle' means any sound-signalling appliance capable of producing the 'short blast' and 'prolonged blast' required by Rule 32, and having an audibility range between 0·5 and 2 miles, depending on the length of the vessel given in Annex III.

The bell and gong must give a clear note. The bell mouth has a diameter of not less than 300 or 200 mm., and if power-driven, the striker should be 3 per cent of the mass of the bell.

The following signals are to be made during fog, mist, falling snow, heavy rainstorms, or other conditions similarly restricting visibility, whether by day or night.

Signals made on the whistle at intervals of not more than 2 minutes

Signal	Signification
One prolonged blast	A power-driven vessel making way through the water
	A pushing vessel rigidly connected to a vessel
Two prolonged blasts in succession	A power-driven vessel underway but stopped and making no way through the water
One prolonged blast followed by two short blasts	A vessel not under command
	A vessel restricted in ability to manoeuvre
	A vessel constrained by her draught
	A sailing vessel
	A vessel engaged in fishing
	A vessel engaged in towing or pushing another vessel

Signal	*Signification*
One prolonged blast followed by three short blasts	A vessel being towed or the last vessel in the tow
One short, one long and one short blast	Additional signal made by a vessel at anchor to give warning to an approaching vessel.
Four short blasts	Pilot vessel underway or at anchor identity signal

Signals made by bell or bell and gong at intervals of not more than 1 minute

Signal	*Signification*
Bell rung rapidly about 5 seconds	Vessel at anchor
Bell rung rapidly followed by Gong sounded rapidly	Vessel over 200 metres at anchor
Bell, 3 distinct strokes Bell rung rapidly Bell, 3 distinct strokes	Vessel aground
Bell, 3 distinct strokes Bell, rung rapidly Bell, 3 distinct strokes Gong sounded rapidly	Vessel over 200 metres aground
Some other efficient sound signal	Vessel less than 12 metres in length at anchor or aground

Sound signals to be made when vessels are in sight of one another
(Manoeuvring and Warning signals)

Signal	*Signification*
One short blast	I am altering my course to starboard
Two short blasts	I am altering my course to port
Three short blasts	I am operating astern propulsion
Five short, rapid blasts	Your intentions or actions not understood
Two long blasts followed by one short blast	I intend to overtake you on your starboard side
Two long blasts followed by two short blasts	I intend to overtake you on your port side
One long, one short, one long and one short blasts (in that order)	I agree to be overtaken
One prolonged blast	Vessel nearing a bend in a channel where other vessels may be obscured
One prolonged blast	An approaching vessel has heard the above

Shape Signals to be exhibited by day are specified in Annex I (6)

Signal	*Signification*
One ball in the forepart	A vessel at anchor
Two balls in a vertical line.	A vessel not under command

Signal	*Signification*
Three balls in a vertical line	A vessel aground
Three shapes in a vertical line, ball, then diamond, then ball	A vessel restricted in ability to manoeuvre
A cylinder	A vessel constrained by her draught
A cone apex downwards	A vessel under sail and power
Two cones in vertical line with their apexes together	A vessel engaged in fishing
A basket	A vessel less than 20 metres fishing
A diamond	A vessel towing. Tow length exceeds 200 metres
A diamond	A vessel being towed. Tow length exceeds 200 metres
Two cones apexes together and a cone apex up in direction of gear	A vessel fishing and gear extends more than 150 metres horizontally
A ball near foremast head and a ball at each yardarm	A vessel engaged in minesweeping
A ball, a diamond, a ball in vertical line	Vessel restricted due to dredging etc., indicating obstruction on side of balls, clear to pass on side of diamonds
Two balls in vertical line on one yardarm	
Two diamonds in vertical line on opposite yardarm	

E

FLASHING, SOUND SIGNALLING, MORSE*

The misuse of sound signalling being of a nature to create serious confusion in the highways at sea, the captains of ships should use these signals with the utmost discretion.

Sound signalling in fog should be reduced to a minimum.

Important Single-letter Signals
(*To be made by flashing or sound*)

A	·—	I have a diver down; keep well clear
F	··—·	I am disabled, communicate with me
K	—·—	I wish to communicate with you
L	·—··	You should stop your vessel instantly
O	———	Man overboard
P	·——·	(By fishing vessels.) My nets have become fast upon an obstruction
U	··—	You are running into danger
V	···—	I require assistance
W	·——	I require medical assistance
Z	——··	I require a tug *or* (When made by fishing vessels near fishing grounds) I am shooting nets

Signals between Ice-breaker and Assisted Vessel(s)

A	·—	Go ahead (proceed along the ice-channel)
G	——·	I am going ahead; follow me
J	·———	Do not follow me (proceed along ice-channel)
P	·——·	Slow down
N	—·	Stop your engines

---

* For a complete list of Single-letter Signals and Towing Signals, and instructions as to their use, see *Brown's Signalling*.

H	**· · · ·**	Reverse your engines
Q	**— — · —**	Shorten distance between vessels
B	**— · · ·**	Increase distance between vessels
Y	**— · — —**	Be ready to take (or cast off) tow line
M	**— —**	My vessel is stopped
4	**· · · · —**	Stop I am ice-bound
5	**· · · · ·**	Attention
†E	**·**	I am altering my course to starboard
†I	**· ·**	I am altering my course to port
†S	**· · ·**	My vessel is stopped and making no way through the water

NOTE—*Signals of letters marked † when made by sound may only be made in compliance with the requirements of the International Regulations for Preventing Collisions at Sea.*

NOTES ON THE REGULATIONS FOR PREVENTING COLLISIONS AT SEA

Part B of the Regulations (Rules 4 to 7) gives all the precautions and considerations to be taken into account in determining if risk of collision exists. Rules 8 to 19 give the action required to avoid collision between vessels of all classes navigating under various circumstances and conditions.

It should be noted that every vessel shall at all times proceed at a safe speed, so that she can take effective action to avoid collision and be stopped within a distance appropriate to the prevailing conditions. Any alteration of course and/or speed to avoid collision should be large enough to be readily apparent to another vessel observing visually or by radar.

Crossing Vessels

On each occasion when a vessel has to keep clear, it is important to remember Rule 15: 'she shall, if the circumstances of the case admit, avoid crossing ahead of the other vessel'. Clearly, when alteration of course is necessary, it must be to pass astern, turn round the other way, or stop.

Under certain circumstances, the give-way vessel may keep clear by maintaining her course and speed. For instance, suppose one vessel to observe both side-lights of another broad on her starboard bow. The first-mentioned vessel is on the 'collision point', and if she maintains her course and speed the other vessel will pass astern.

When the bearing of a crossing vessel alters appreciably there can be no risk of collision, the crossing point must be ahead or astern.

Always take a compass bearing on a light when it comes

into view. Note any alteration or otherwise in the bearing, then if both vessels maintain their course and speed, bear in mind the following rules, viz:—

(1) **If the bearing remains constant, a collision must occur.**

(2) **If the bearing draws ahead, the other vessel will pass ahead of you.**

(3) **If the bearing draws aft, you will pass ahead of the other vessel.**

As these Rules are most important and should be thoroughly understood, the following diagrams (*a*), (*b*) and (*c*) will illustrate their meaning.

In Diagram (A), vessel *A*, steering North, observes vessel *B* bearing N. 60° E. After an interval *A* when in position *A'*

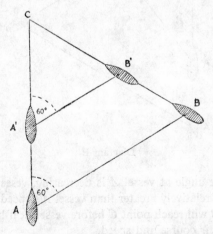

Diagram A

again takes a bearing of vessel *B*, which is now in position *B'*, and finds her bearing N. 60° E., i.e. bearing remaining

AB is therefore parallel to *A'B'* and triangles *ACB* and *A'CB'* are congruent. Hence if both vessels maintain their course and speed, they must meet at point *C*, which is the 'collision point'.

In Diagram (B), vessel *A* steering North sights vessel *B* bearing N. 60° E. When *A* is in position *A'* vessel *B* is in position *B'* and now bears from *A* N. 40° E., i.e. the bearing is drawing ahead.

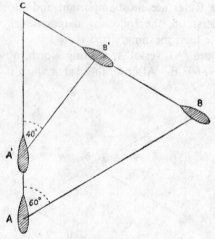

Diagram B

Since the angle at vessel *A* is decreasing, vessel *B*'s speed along *BC* is relatively greater than vessel *A*'s speed along *AC*, and vessel *B* will reach point *C* before vessel *A*, if both vessels maintain their course and speed.

In Diagram (C), vessel *A* observes vessel *B* to bear 60° on her starboard bow. After an interval vessel *A*, when in position *A'*, again takes a bearing of vessel *B* and finds *B'* now bearing 75° on the starboard bow, i.e. the bearing is drawing astern.

The increase in the bearing indicates that vessel *B*'s speed along *BC* is relatively less than vessel *A*'s speed along *AC* and in consequence vessel *A* will arrive at point *C* before vessel *B*, assuming, of course, that both vessels maintain their course and speed.

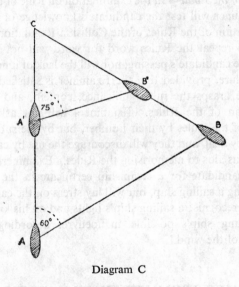

Diagram C

Two Power-driven Vessels Meeting End On

It is of interest to note that only in one case the Regulations for Preventing Collisions at Sea distinctly specify the manner in which vessels must keep clear of each other, and that is when two power-driven vessels are meeting end on or nearly end on, i.e. when each vessel sees both side-lights of the other, or in daytime the masts of each other in line, each must then alter course to starboard.

EXTRACT FROM REGULATIONS FOR THE EXAMINATION OF MASTERS AND MATES

Rule of the Road—'In the examination on Rule of the Road, the Examiner will test the candidate's knowledge of the sense and intention of the Rules of the Collision Regulations. Mere ability to repeat the Rules word for word will not suffice to ensure the candidate's passing, nor will the lack of it necessarily entail failure, provided that the Examiner is satisfied that the candidate grasps the full significance, content, and practical application of the Rules. Examiners will not ask for the content of the Rules by their number, but by the subject with which they deal, and they will discourage the use by candidates of verses as aids to memorising the Rules. Examiners will not place a candidate for a steamship certificate in the position of handling a sailing ship, but will lay stress on the candidate's ability to recognise a sailing ship's lights and on his knowledge of a sailing ship's possible manoeuvres according to the direction of the wind.'

EXTRACTS FROM MERCHANT SHIPPING ACT
Observance of Collision Regulations

All owners and masters of ships shall obey the Collision Regulations, and shall not carry or exhibit any other lights, or use any other fog signals, than such as are required by those Regulations.

If an infringement of the Collision Regulations is caused by the wilful default of the master or owner of the ship, that master or owner shall, in respect of each offence be guilty of a misdemeanour.

If any damage to person or property arises from the non-observance by any ship of any of the Collision Regulations, the damage shall be deemed to have been occasioned by the wilful default of the person in charge of the deck of the ship at the time, unless it is shown to the satisfaction of the Court that the circumstances of the case made a departure from the Regulations necessary.

Where in a case of collision it is proved to the Court before whom the case is tried that any of the Collision Regulations have been infringed, the ship by which the Regulation has been infringed shall be deemed to be in fault, unless it is shown to the satisfaction of the Court that the circumstances of the case made departure from the Regulation necessary.

The Dept. of Trade shall furnish a copy of the Collision Regulations to any master or owner of a ship who applies for it.

Duty of Vessel to Assist the other in Case of Collision

In every case of collision between two vessels, it shall be the duty of the master or person in charge of each vessel, if and so far as he can do so without danger to his own vessel, crew and passengers (if any).

(a) to render to the other vessel, her master, crew and passengers (if any) such assistance as may be practicable, and may be necessary to save them from any danger caused by the collision, and to stay by the other vessel until he has ascertained that she has no need of further assistance; and also

(b) to give to the master or person in charge of the other

vessel the name of his own vessel and of the port to which she belongs, and also the names of the ports from which she comes and to which she is bound.

If the master or person in charge fails without reasonable cause to comply with this section, he shall be guilty of a misdemeanour, and, if he is a certificated officer, an inquiry into his conduct may be held and his certificate cancelled or suspended.

Collisions to be Entered in Official Log

In every case of collision, in which it is practicable so to do, the master of every ship shall immediately after the occurrence cause a statement thereof and of the circumstances under which the same occurred, to be entered in the official log book (if any and the entry shall be signed by the master, and also by the mate or one of the crew.

If the master fails to comply with this section, he shall for each offence be liable to a fine not exceeding twenty pounds.

REPORT OF ACCIDENTS AND LOSS OF SHIP

Report to Board of Trade of Accidents to Steamships

When a steamship has sustained or caused any accident occasioning loss of life or any serious injury to any person, or has received any material damage affecting her seaworthiness or her efficiency either in her hull or in any part of her machinery, the owner or master shall, within twenty-four hours after the happening of the accident or damage, or as soon thereafter as possible, transmit to the Department of Trade, by letter signed by the owner or master a report of the accident or damage, and of the probable occasion thereof, stating the name of the ship, her official number (if any), the port to which she belongs, and the place where she is.

If the owner or master of a steamship fails without reasonable cause to comply with this section, he shall for each offence be liable to a fine not exceeding fifty pounds.

This section shall apply to all British ships, and to all foreign steamships carrying passengers between places in the United Kingdom.

A CROSS-EXAMINATION

To enable the candidate to test his knowledge of the Regulations for Preventing Collisions at Sea.

The Questions should be taken in the given order as in many instances they lead up to each other.

---

1. *Q.*—Are the Regulations for Preventing Collisions at Sea applicable only to vessels on the high seas?
   Ans.—No. They refer to all waters connected therewith navigable by sea-going vessels.

2. *Q.*—What document is accepted as giving the correct length and breadth of a vessel?
   Ans.—Her Certificate of Registry.

3. *Q.*—In the case of a seaplane what document gives its maximum length and span?
   Ans.—Its Certificate of Airworthiness. In the absence of this certificate the dimensions are found by measurement.

4. *Q.*—Define the terms, 'short blast' and 'prolonged blast'.
   Ans.—A 'short blast' is a blast of about one second's duration. A 'prolonged blast' is a blast of from four to six seconds' duration.

5. *Q.*—What does the term 'power-driven' vessel mean?
   Ans.—It means any vessel propelled by machinery.

6. *Q.*—When is a power-driven vessel considered a sailing vessel?
   Ans.—When she is under sail only.

7. *Q.*—When is a vessel, or seaplane on the water, 'under-way'?

   Ans.—When she is not at anchor or made fast to the shore, or aground.

8. *Q.*—Has the word 'visible' any qualification when employed in the Rules?

   Ans.—Yes. It means visible on a dark night with a clear atmosphere.

9. *Q.*—During what hours must all lights mentioned in the Rules be exhibited?

   Ans.—From sunset to sunrise in all weathers.

10. *Q.*—What precautions must be taken with regard to lights on a vessel other than those she is required to exhibit?

    Ans.—No other lights shall be exhibited except such lights as cannot be mistaken for the prescribed lights or impair their visibility or distinctive character, or interfere with the keeping of a proper lookout.

11. *Q.*—Of what colour and how far visible must a power-driven vessel's masthead lights be seen?

    Ans.—Bright white lights visible 6 miles. (Rule 22.)

12. *Q.*—Over how many points of the compass must they show?

    Ans.—Over an arc of the horizon of 20 points of the compass (225°).

13. *Q.*—Where must they be carried?

    Ans.—One on or in front of the foremast, or if a vessel without a foremast then in the forepart of the vessel, and a second white light either forward or abaft the former white light. Vessels of less than 50 metres in length and vessels engaged in towing shall not be required to carry the second white light, but may do so.

14. *Q.*—Is a power-driven vessel compelled to carry two masthead lights?

   Ans.—Only if of 50 metres or upwards in length.

15. *Q.*—What is the advantage of two masthead lights compared with one?

   Ans.—When two masthead lights are carried an observer can discern with some degree of accuracy the direction in which the vessel is heading. When the two lights appear in a vertical line, one over the other, the vessel is end on. When the horizontal distance between the lights is much greater than the vertical distance, the vessel's course is approaching a direction at right angles to the observer.

16. *Q.*—How far must a power-driven vessel's sidelights be visible?

   Ans.—At least 3 or 2 miles.   (Rule 22.)

17. *Q.*—On which side must the green light be carried, and on what side the red?

   Ans.—The green on the starboard side, the red on the port side.

18. *Q.*—Over what arc must each light show?

   Ans.—Over an arc of the horizon of 10 points of the compass ($112\frac{1}{2}°$) from right ahead to 2 points ($22\frac{1}{2}°$) abaft the beam.

19. *Q.*—What precautions must be taken to prevent either light from being seen across the other bow?

   Ans.—They must be fitted with inboard screens which are painted matt black.

20. *Q.*—What vessel, in addition to her sidelights, carries two bright white lights in a vertical line, one over the other?

   Ans.—A power-driven vessel towing, or pushing another vessel.

21. *Q.*—Is she ever compelled to carry three bright white lights in a vertical line, one over the other?

Ans.—Yes, when the length of the tow exceeds 200 metres.

22. How is the length of the tow measured?

Ans.—From the stern of the towing vessel to the stern of the last vessel towed.

23. *Q.*—How far apart are these bright white lights to be?

Ans.—At least 2 metres apart, vertically.

24. *Q.*—If the three are carried, at what height above the hull must be the lowest?

Ans.—Not less than 4 metres.

25. *Q.*—Is a vessel when towing compelled to carry a light aft for the vessel towed to steer by?

Ans.—The towing vessel shall exhibit a yellow towing light in a vertical line above the stern light. The towing light has the same range and characteristics as the stern light.

26. *Q.*—What lights must a sailing vessel show when underway?

Ans.—Sidelights and stern light.

27. *Q.*—Does a vessel not under command, or a vessel laying or picking up a submarine cable, carry sidelights?

Ans.—Yes, if making way through the water; otherwise not.

28. *Q.*—What special distinguishing lights must a vessel show when not under command, but underway?

Ans.—Two red lights.

29. *Q.*—At what part of the vessel must they be carried?

Ans.—Where they can best be seen. At the same height as a power-driven vessel's masthead light, and if a power-driven vessel then in place of the light, or lights.

30. *Q.*—In what position must the two red lights be carried with reference to each other?

    Ans.—In a vertical position, one over the other, not less than 2 metres apart.

31. *Q.*—How far and over what arc must they be visible?

    Ans.—At least three miles, all round the horizon.

32. *Q.*—What distinguishing mark does a vessel not under command, but underway, carry by day?

    Ans.—Two black balls or shapes, each not less than 0·6 metre in diameter.

33. *Q.*—At what part of the vessel and in what position with respect to each other?

    Ans.—Where they can best be seen; in a vertical line, one over the other, and not less than 2 metres apart.

34. *Q.*—What special distinguishing lights does a vessel carry when employed in laying or picking up a submarine cable or navigation mark, or a vessel engaged in surveying or underwater operations, when by the nature of her work she is unable to get out of the way of approaching vessels?

    Ans.—Three lights in a vertical line, one over the other, not less than 2 metres apart, the highest and lowest red, and the middle one white.

35. *Q.*—How far and over what arc must they be visible?

    Ans.—Not less than 3 miles, all round the horizon.

36. *Q.*—From what part of the vessel must they be exhibited?

    Ans.—Where they can best be seen. The shapes to be equally spaced and the lower one at least 4 metres above the hull.

37. *Q.*—What does she show by day?

    Ans.—Three shapes, each not less than 0·6 metre in

diameter, one over the other and not less than 2 metres apart; the highest and lowest globular in shape and the middle one diamond in shape, all black in colour.

38. *Q.*—From what part of the vessel must these shapes be exhibited?

    Ans.—Where they can best be seen.

39. *Q.*—Is the exhibition of the foregoing signals and lights to be taken as an indication that the vessel showing them is in distress and requires assistance?

    Ans.—No, only that she is not under command or is unable to get out of the way.

40. *Q.*—What additional lights are carried when a vessel is restricted in her ability to deviate from her course because of her draught and the available depth of water?

    Ans.—Three all-round red lights in a vertical line where they can best be seen, and visible for at least 3 miles. By day she carries a black cylinder where it can best be seen.

41. *Q.*—What additional light is exhibited by an air-cushion vessel operating in the non-displacement mode?

    Ans.—An all-round flashing yellow light, visible for at least 3 miles or, if the length of the vessel is less than 50 metres, 2 miles.

42. *Q.*—In what manner may the bright white light of a power-driven vessel of less than 12 metres in length differ from that of similar vessel of larger tonnage?

    Ans.—It need only be carried not less than 2·5 metres above the gunwale and be visible 3 miles.

43. *Q.*—Is any modification permitted in the style of sidelights for these vessels?

F

Ans.—Yes; they need only be visible 1 mile, and they may be carried either in the manner prescribed for large power-driven vessels or in a combined lantern which shows a green light and a red light from right ahead to two points abaft the beam on their respective sides.

44. *Q.*—In what position must this combined light be carried with reference to the bright white light?

Ans.—Not less than 1 metre below it.

45. *Q.*—Are there exceptions to the lights prescribed for a power-driven vessel?

Ans.—Yes. If the length of the vessel is less than 7 metres and maximum speed not more than 7 knots she may exhibit an all round white light. She shall also exhibit sidelights if practicable.

46. *Q.*—What is a Manoeuvring Light?

Ans.—An all-round white light which is flashed to supplement the whistle signal on one, two or three short blasts required by Rule 34. The light should be at least 2 metres above the masthead light provided that it shall be carried not less than 2 metres above or below the after masthead light.

47. *Q.*—What light must a sailing vessel under 7 metres or a vessel under oars carry?

Ans.—If she does not carry sidelights and a stern light she must have ready at hand a lighted lantern or an electric torch showing a white light to be exhibited in sufficient time to prevent collision.

48. *Q.*—Are power-driven vessels of less than 7 metres, and vessels under oars or sails of less than 7 metres, when not under command, required to show the special lights prescribed for vessels of larger tonnage?

Ans.—No.

49. *Q.*—Describe the lights to be carried by a seaplane underway on the water?

Ans.—A seaplane on the water exhibits the same lights and shapes as required for a power-driven vessel. Where it is impracticable for a seaplane to exhibit lights and shapes of the characteristics or in the positions prescribed, she shall exhibit lights and shapes as closely similar as possible.

50. *Q.*—What lights are exhibited by a vessel on pilotage duty?

Ans.—Two all-round lights in a vertical line near the masthead, the upper being white and the lower red, visible 3 miles. In addition, when underway sidelights and a stern light; and when at anchor the anchor light, lights or shape.

51. *Q.*—What lights are exhibited by a pilot vessel not on pilotage duty?

Ans.—The lights prescribed for a similar vessel of her length.

52 *Q.*—What lights must fishing vessels carry when underway, but not fishing?

Ans.—The lights prescribed for similar vessels of their tonnage.

53. *Q.*—Describe the lights to be shown by vesssels engaged in fishing, except trawling, with gear extending not more than 150 metres horizontally into the seaway.

Ans.—They shall carry two lights in a vertical line, one over the other. The upper shall be red and the lower light white and each shall be visible all round the horizon. The lower of these two lights shall be carried at a height above the sidelights not less than twice the distance between the two vertical lights. When making way they carry sidelights and stern light as prescribed in Rule 22.

54. *Q.*—What lights are to be shown by vessels fishing, except trawling, if the gear extends more than 500 feet into the seaway?

Ans.—In addition to the lights mentioned above she carries a white light visible all round the horizon at a distance of not less than 2 metres nor more than 6 metres in the direction of the outlying gear. The height of this light shall not exceed the height of the white light nor be lower than the sidelights.

55. *Q.*—What is the day signal for vessels engaged in fishing?

Ans.—They display where it can best be seen a black shape consisting of two cones, each not less than 0·6 metre in diameter with their points together, one above the other. When their fishing gear extends more than 150 metres into the seaway they display an additional black conical shape, point upwards, in the direction of the outlying gear.

56. *Q.*—What day signal may a vessel of less than 20 metres show when fishing?

Ans.—They may substitute a basket for the black shape.

57. *Q.*—What constitutes 'trawling' within the meaning of Rule 26?

Ans.—By trawling is meant the dragging of a dredge net or other apparatus through the water.

58. *Q.*—If a vessel fishing with purse seine nets becomes hampered by its gear what additional lights may be exhibited?

Ans.—Two yellow lights in a vertical line flashing alternately every second. This signal is given when other fishing vessels are in close proximity.

59. *Q.*—May vessels fishing use working lights?

    Ans.—Yes, but the fishermen must take into account that specially bright or insufficiently screened working lights may impair the visibility and distinctive character of the lights required to be carried.

60. *Q.*—What lights may a vessel engaged in fishing show in order to attract the attention of an approaching vessel?

    Ans.—They may use a flare-up light or may direct the beam of their searchlight in the direction of a danger to the approaching vessel, in such a way as not to embarrass other vessels.

61. *Q.*—How far must all lights prescribed for fishing vessels be visible?

    Ans.—At least two miles.

62. *Q.*—A vessel engaged in trawling may carry the white masthead light prescribed in Rule 22. If she does so, where must it be placed?

    Ans.—It must be higher than and abaft the all-round green and white lights.

63. *Q.*—What light must a vessel, when underway, carry at her stern?

    Ans.—A white light so fixed as to show over an arc of the horizon of 135° to 67½° from right aft on each side.

64. *Q.*—Are there any other requirements specified for the stern light?

    Ans.—Yes, it must be carried as nearly as practicable on the same level as the sidelights and be visible for a distance of at least 3 miles.

65. *Q.*—In the case of a small vessel is it necessary for the stern light to be fixed in position?

    Ans.—In a small vessel if it is not possible on account of bad weather or other causes for the light to be fixed, an electric torch or a lighted lantern shall be kept at hand and on the approach of an overtaking vessel shown in sufficient time to prevent collision.

66. *Q.*—What light and how far visible does a vessel under 50 metres in length show when at anchor?

Ans.—A white light in a lantern showing a clear, uniform and unbroken light visible all round the horizon at a distance of at least 2 miles.

67. *Q.*—At what part of the vessel must it be carried?

Ans.—In the forepart of the vessel where it can best be seen.

68. *Q.*—In what way do the requirements differ for a vessel of 50 metres in length and upwards?

Ans.—She must carry the white light in the forepart of the vessel at a height of not less than 6 metres above the hull and in addition she must show a similar light at or near the stern not less than 4·5 metres lower than the forward light.

69. *Q.*—How far must these lights be visible?

Ans.—Both lights shall be visible all round the horizon at a distance of at least 3 miles.

70. *Q.*—Between sunrise and sunset how does a vessel indicate she is at anchor?

Ans.—She must carry in the forepart of the vessel, where it can best be seen, one black ball not less than 0·6 metre in diameter.

71. *Q.*—What lights does a vessel show when engaged in laying or picking up a submarine cable, or in surveying or underwater operations, and at anchor?

Ans.—She shows the red, white and red lights, as pre-

scribed by Rule 27 and the anchor lights required for
her length.

72. *Q.*—How would such a vessel when at anchor indicate her
occupation between sunrise and sunset?

Ans.—Show the ball, diamond and ball shapes as required
by Rule 27 and the anchor ball.

73. *Q.*—What lights does a vessel show when aground?

Ans.—The two red lights, prescribed for a vessel not under
command and the anchor lights required for her length.

74. *Q.*—What shapes does a vessel show during daytime when
aground?

Ans.—Three black balls, each not less than 0·6 metre in
diameter and not less than 1·5 metre apart in a vertical
line, one over the other, where they can best be seen.

75. *Q.*—In addition to showing the regulation lights required
of her what may a vessel, or seaplane on the water, do
in order to attract attention?

Ans.—She may show a flare-up light or use a detonating or
other sound signal that cannot be mistaken for any
signal authorised elsewhere under the rules.

76. *Q.*—What is the day signal for a vessel proceeding under
sail and also being propelled by machinery?

Ans.—She shall carry forward, where it can best be seen,
one black conical shape, point downwards, not less than
0·6 metre in diameter at its base.

77. *Q.*—What is required of every vessel, or seaplane when
taxi-ing on the water, in fog, mist, falling snow, heavy
rainstorms or other condition restricting visibility?

Ans.—She shall go at a safe speed, having regard to the
existing circumstances and conditions and make certain
sound signals according to her class.

78. *Q.*—With what apparatus must every power-driven vessel be provided with for this purpose?

Ans.—She must be provided with an efficient 'whistle', as defined in Rule 32 as any signalling appliance capable of producing the prescribed blasts and which complies with the specifications of Annex III, and also with an efficient bell. A vessel over 100 metres shall be provided with a gong in addition to the bell.

79. *Q.*—What apparatus is a sailing vessel of 7 metres or upwards compelled to carry?

Ans.—A 'whistle' or similar appliance as required by Rule 32 and a bell.

80. *Q.*—What should be the approximate audible range of a whistle in conditions of still air on board a ship having average background noise level?

Ans.—If the length of the vessel is over 200 metres; range 2 miles. If the length of the vessel is 75 to 200 metres; range 1·5 miles. If the length of the vessel is 20 to 75 metres; range 1·0 miles. If the length of the vessel is less than 20 metres; range 0·5 miles.

81. *Q.*—What is the fog-signal for a power-driven vessel making way through the water?

Ans.—Sound at intervals of not more than 2 minutes a prolonged blast.

82. *Q.*—What is the fog-signal for a power-driven vessel underway but stopped and making no way through the water?

Ans.—Sound at intervals of not more than 2 minutes two prolonged blasts, with an interval of about 1 second between them.

83. *Q.*—What is the fog-signal for a sailing vessel underway?

Ans.—Sound at intervals of not more than 2 minutes

three blasts in succession, namely one long followed
by two short blasts. (Vessel restricted in her ability
to manoeuvre.)

84. *Q.*—What is the fog-signal for a vessel at anchor?

Ans.—Ring the bell rapidly for about 5 seconds at intervals
of not more than 1 minute.

If more than 100 metres in length the bell shall be
sounded in the forepart of the vessel and in the after-
part of the vessel a gong or other instrument sounded
for about 5 seconds at intervals of not more than
1 minute. The tone and sounding of the gong or other
instrument is not to be confused with that of the bell.

85. *Q.*—May a vessel at anchor make an additional signal to
give warning of her position to an approaching vessel?

Ans.—Yes, she may sound three blasts in succession,
namely one short, one prolonged and one short blast.

86. *Q.*—What fog-signal must a vessel make when she is
towing?

Ans.—Sound at intervals of not more than 2 minutes,
three blasts in succession, one prolonged blast followed
by two short blasts.

87. *Q.*—What is the fog-signal for a vessel being towed?

Ans.—Sound at intervals of not more than 2 minutes, four
blasts in succession, one prolonged blast followed by
three short blasts. If more than one vessel is towed only
the last vessel of the tow, if manned, shall make the
signal and when practicable this signal shall be made
immediately after the signal made by the towing vessel.

88. *Q.*—What is the fog-signal for a vessel aground?

Ans.—The signal for a vessel at anchor according to her
length and in addition, give three separate and distinct

strokes on the bell immediately before and after the bell signal.

89. *Q*.—If a vessel of less than 12 metres, a rowing boat or seaplane on the water do not make the foregoing fog signals, what must they do?

Ans.—They shall make some other efficient sound signal at intervals of not more than 2 minutes.

90. *Q*.—What is the fog-signal for a vessel engaged in fishing?

Ans.—At intervals of not more than 2 minutes sound three blasts in succession, namely one prolonged blast followed by two short blasts.

91. *Q*.—What is required of a power-driven vessel hearing apparently forward of her beam the fog-signal of a vessel, the position of which is not ascertained?

Ans.—She shall, so far as the circumstances of the case admit, stop her engines and then navigate with caution until danger of collision is over.

92. *Q*.—In obeying and construing the Steering and Sailing Rules what conditions or considerations should govern any action taken?

Ans.—Any action taken should be positive, taken in ample time and with due regard to the observance of good seamanship.

93. *Q*.—When two vessels are approaching each other, how can it be ascertained whether risk of collision exists or not?

Ans.—By carefully watching the compass bearing of the approaching vessel. If the bearing does not appreciably change such risk should be deemed to exist.

94. *Q*.—When two sailing vessels are approaching one another so as to involve risk of collision, which one keeps out of the way of the other?

Ans.—It depends entirely how each has the wind with respect to the other. The action to be taken under the different contingencies that may arise being given in Rule 12.

95. *Q.*—Enunciate the Rule.

Ans.— (i) When each has the wind on a different side, the vessel which has the wind on the port side shall keep out of the way of the other.

(ii) When both have the wind on the same side, the vessel which is to windward shall keep out of the way of the vessel which is to leeward.

96. *Q.*—When two power-driven vessels are meeting on reciprocal courses, so as to involve risk of collision, which one keeps out of the way of the other?

Ans.—Each shall alter her course to starboard so that each may pass on the port side of the other.

97. *Q.*—State clearly the only cases to which this rule applies·

Ans.—The only cases to which it does apply are, when each of the two vessels is end on, or nearly end on, to the other; in other words, to cases in which by day, each vessel sees the masts of the other in a line, or nearly in a line, with her own; and by night to cases in which each vessel is in a position as to see both the sidelights of the other.

98. *Q.*—When two power-driven vessels are crossing so as to involve risk of collision, which vessel keeps out of the way of the other?

Ans.—The vessel which has the other on her own starboard side.

99. *Q.*—When a power-driven vessel and a sailing vessel are approaching each other so as to involve risk of collision,

which vessel keeps clear of the other?

Ans.—The power-driven vessel.

100. *Q.*—In narrow channels what precautions must be taken by a sailing vessel?

Ans.—She must not impede the safe passage of a power-driven vessel following a traffic-lane or navigating in a narrow channel.

101. *Q.*—Where, by any of the Rules, one of the two vessels is to keep out of the way, what is required of the other?

Ans.—She shall keep her course and speed.

102. *Q.*—Does Rule 17 modify this direction in any way?

Ans.—Yes, it states. When, from any cause, the latter vessel finds herself so close that collision cannot be avoided by the action of the giving-way vessel alone, she also shall take such action as will best aid to avert collision.

103. *Q.*—Does any other Rule sanction in special circumstances a departure from the general Rules?

Ans.—Yes, Rule 2 states: 'In obeying and construing these Rules due regard shall be had to all dangers of navigation and collision and to any special circumstances, including the limitations of the craft involved, which may render a departure from the above Rules necessary in order to avoid immediate danger.'

104. *Q.*—What other Rule whilst calling attention to all the usual precautions to be taken, also calls for the exercise of personal intelligence on the arising of any unforseen circumstances?

Ans.—Rule 2(a), which states: 'Nothing in these Rules shall exonerate any vessel, or the owner, Master or crew thereof, from the consequences of any neglect to carry lights or signals, or of any neglect to keep a proper lookout, or of the neglect of any precaution which may be required by the ordinary practice of seamen, or by the special circumstances of the case.'

105. *Q.*—Every vessel must proceed at a 'safe speed'; how is this speed determined?

Ans.—By taking into account the prevailing visibility and weather conditions, the traffic density, the ship's turning and stopping ability and the draught with reference to the depth of water.

106. *Q.*—What are the responsibilities of a seaplane on the water?

Ans.—In general, a seaplane keeps well clear of all vessels, but where risk of collision exists she complies with Rule 18 for a power-driven vessel.

107. *Q.*—When one vessel is overtaking another, which one keeps out of the way?

Ans.—In all cases the overtaking vessel, Rule 13 (*a*) states: 'Notwithstanding anything contained in these Rules, every vessel overtaking any other shall keep out of the way of the overtaken vessel.'

108. *Q.*—Is it necessary that one vessel should be following up in the other's wake in order to be considered an 'overtaking vessel'?

Ans.—No. Provided that she is coming up from any direction more than 2 points (22½°) abaft the other vessel's beam she is deemed an 'overtaking vessel'.

109. *Q.*—What proof would the overtaking vessel have by night that she was in that position with reference to the other?

Ans.—The fact that she was unable to see the other vessel's sidelights.

110. *Q.*—What proof would she have by day?

   Ans.—None. It would be a matter of judgment, but if lack of certainty exists, Rule 13 (*c*) stipulates that she shall assume that she is an overtaking vessel and keep out of the way.

111. *Q.*—Would any subsequent alteration of the bearing between the two vessels make the overtaking vessel a 'crossing vessel' and relieve her of the responsibilities of an overtaking vessel?

   Ans.—No subsequent alteration of the bearing between the two vessels shall make the overtaking vessel a crossing vessel within the meaning of the Rule, or relieve her of the duty of keeping clear of the overtaken vessel until she is finally past and clear.

112. *Q.*—What provision is made with respect to the navigating of narrow channels by power-driven vessels?

   Ans.—In narrow channels every power-driven vessel when proceeding along the course of the channel shall, when it is safe and practicable, keep to that side of the fairway or mid-channel which lies on the starboard side of such vessel.

113. *Q.*—When a power-driven vessel is nearing a bend in a channel is she required to indicate her approach to the bend?

   Ans.—Yes. Whenever a power-driven vessel is nearing a bend in a channel, where a power-driven vessel approaching from the other direction cannot be seen, she shall, having arrived within one-half mile of the bend give a signal of one prolonged blast of her whistle. This signal of one blast shall be answered by a similar blast given by any approaching power-driven vessel that may be within hearing around the bend.

114. *Q.*—Is there any instruction regarding the rounding of a bend in a channel?

   Ans.—Yes, the bend shall be rounded with alertness and caution.

115. *Q.*—What protection is afforded fishing vessels when engaged in their vocation?

   Ans.—All vessels not engaged in fishing shall, when under way, keep out of the way of any vessels fishing with nets or lines or trawls.

116. *Q.*—Is a fishing vessel thereby allowed unbridled licence and freedom from all responsibility?

   Ans.—No, she shall not impede the passage of other vessels in a narrow channel or fairway, and keeps clear of vessels restricted or not under command.

117. *Q.*—In taking any course authorised or required by the Rules what signal is a power-driven vessel required to make on her whistle when the vessels are in sight of one another?

   Ans.—One short blast to mean, 'I am altering my course to starboard.' Two short blasts to mean, 'I am altering my course to port.' Three short blasts to mean, 'I am operating astern propulsion.'

118. *Q.*—What reservation is made in the Regulations to allow for local legislation with respect to the navigating of harbours, inland waters, etc.?

   Ans.—Rule 1 states: 'Nothing in these Rules shall interfere with the operation of special rules made by an appropriate authority for roadsteads, harbours, rivers, lakes or inland waterways connected with the high seas and navigable by seagoing vessels.'

119. *Q.*—What are the signals of distress to be used or

displayed by a vessel or seaplane on the water requiring assistance from other vessels or from the shore?

Ans.—The following signals shall be used or displayed, either together or separately:—

    (i) A gun or other explosive signal fired at intervals of about a minute.

    (ii) A continuous sounding, with any fog-signal apparatus.

    (iii) Rockets or shells, throwing red stars fired one at a time at short intervals.

    (iv) A signal made by radiotelegraphy or by any other signalling method consisting of the group ▪ ▪ ▪ ▬ ▬ ▬ ▪ ▪ ▪ in the Morse Code.

    (v) A signal sent by radiotelephony consisting of the spoken word 'May Day'.

    (vi) The International Code Signal of distress indicated by N.C.

    (vii) A signal consisting of a square flag having above or below it a ball or anything resembling a ball.

    (viii) Flames on the vessel (as from a burning tar barrel, oil barrel, etc.).

    (ix) A rocket parachute flare or a hand flare showing a red light.

    (x) A smoke signal giving off a volume of orange-coloured smoke.

    (xi) Slowly and repeatedly raising and lowering arms outstretched to each side.

    (xii) The radiotelegraph alarm signal.

    (xiii) The radiotelephone alarm signal.

(xiv) Signals transmitted by emergency position-indicating radio beacons.

NOTE—The radio telegraph alarm signal consists of twelve dashes of 4 seconds duration with an interval of 1 second between consecutive dashes. This is designed to actuate the auto alarms of vessels so fitted.

The radiotelephone alarm signal consists of 2 tones transmitted alternately over periods of from 30 seconds to 1 minute.

G

TO DETERMINE THE DIRECTION IN WHICH A POWER-DRIVEN VESSEL IS HEADING

As previously mentioned, during the light of day the mariner will be seldom in doubt as to the course of an approaching vessel. At night, however, on observing a vessel's lights, this information can only be obtained after making certain deductions, and even then, in most cases, only an approximation is established.

The major part of the examination relating to the 'Rule of the Road'—a most rigorous and searching test—is confined to ascertaining the candidate's knowledge with respect to the correct action to take on observing the lights of different types of vessels and the procedure to be adopted in fog.

A model of a power-driven or sailing vessel, of which the candidate is assumed to be in charge, is placed on a table and a metal plate with coloured magnets representing various lights are then placed in certain positions. The candidate must then indicate whether he would 'stand on' or 'keep clear'. To give the correct answer it is necessary to know the direction in which the other vessel is heading.

We shall now proceed to show how this information may be deduced.

All sidelights show over an arc of 10 points of the compass, from right ahead to 2 points abaft the beam and provide a ready means of determining the possible directions in which a vessel may be heading.

When the sidelight of a power-driven vessel is seen, it is a simple matter to find the arc within which she must be heading, but when the sidelight is that of a sailing vessel the direction

94

of the wind must be taken into consideration when calculating the arc. For the present we shall confine our attention to power-driven vessels, leaving the case of sailing vessels till a later stage.

To obtain the desired information proceed as follows:—
Take a bearing of the light. Reverse the bearing and allow 10 points to the right or left in accordance with the following rules:—

(1) For a Red light, allow 10 points to the Right of the reversed bearing.

(2) For a Green light, allow 10 points to the Left of the reversed bearing.

In each case the result is the arc through which the vessel can swing and still exhibit the red or green light respectively.

Example—From a vessel heading **W.S.W.** the green side-light of a power-driven vessel bears **N.W.** Find the arc within which the vessel is heading.

The reverse of **N.W.** is **S.E.** Apply Rule (2).

Ten points to the left of **S.E.** gives **N.N.E.**

The vessel must be heading between **S.E.** and **N.N.E.**

Example—From a vessel heading North, the red light of a power-driven vessel is observed to bear **N.E. by N.** Find the arc within which the vessel must be heading.

The reversed bearing is **S.W. by S.** Apply Rule (1).

Ten points to the right of **S.W. by S.** gives **N.W. by N.**

The vessel is therefore heading between **S.W. by S.** and **N.W. by N.**

Diagram No. 1 will make this clear.

The observer is in vessel *A*, situated in the centre of the compass. *B* is the vessel whose red light is observed bearing **N.E. by N.**, i.e. *AB*, from vessel *A*. *BD* is the reverse of *AB*. *DC* is an arc of 10 points of the compass to the right of *BD*

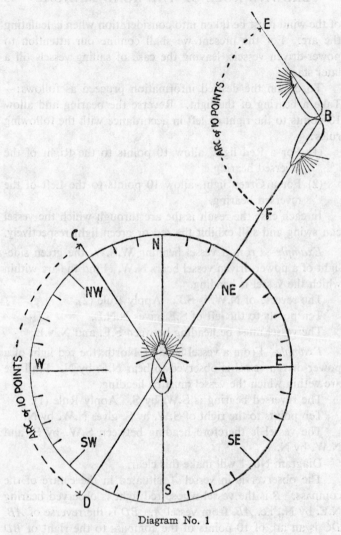

Diagram No. 1

and is the arc through which vessel *B* can swing and still show her red light to vessel *A*, because:—

DC and *FE* are each arcs of 10 points of the compass, therefore *AC* and *BE* are parallel lines.

Suppose vessel *B* were heading to the Southward of *BF*, then her green light would be open.

Now, suppose vessel *B* were heading to the Northward of *BE*, then *BF* would be more than 2 points abaft her beam, and the red light would not be visible to vessel *A*. Thus it follows that vessel *B* must be heading between **S.W. by S.** and **N.W. by N.**

It should here be remarked that were vessel *B* heading **S.W. by S.**, then **both** her sidelights would be visible to vessel *A*, and in order to shut out her green light *B* would have to be heading **S.W. by S.** (westerly). It is usual, however, to reckon that only one sidelight is visible within the 10 points. If necessary, qualify your answer by the insertion of the word *nearly* as in the following questions, which, if thoroughly worked out, *without the assistance of a compass card*, will prove excellent mental exercise, and will be of the greatest value to young seamen who are but indifferent hands at 'boxing the compass'.

You are told how a certain coloured light of a power-driven vessel bears, and are required to state the points between which the vessel showing it must be heading.

1. *Q.*—You are heading **N.** and see a vessel's red light 4 points on your starboard bow; how must she be heading?

   Ans.—Between **S.W.** nearly and **N.N.W.**

2. *Q.*—You are heading **N.** and see a vessel's green light 2 points on your port bow; how must she be heading?

   Ans.—Between **S.S.E.** nearly and **N.E.**

3. *Q.*—You are heading **E.** and see a vessel's red light 2 points on your starboard bow; how must she be heading?

   Ans.—Between **W.N.W.** nearly and **N.E.**

4. *Q.*—You are heading **W.** and see a vessel's green light 4 points on your port bow; how must she be heading?

   Ans.—Between **N.E.** nearly and **W.N.W.**

5. *Q.*—You are heading **S.** and see a vessel's red light 2 points on your starboard bow; how must she be heading?

   Ans.—Between **N.N.E.** nearly and **S.E.**

6. *Q.*—You are heading **S.** and see a vessel's green light 4 points on your port bow; how must she be heading?

   Ans.—Between **N.W.** nearly and **S.S.W.**

7. *Q.*—You are heading **S.** and see a vessel's red light 4 points on your starboard bow; how must she be heading?

   Ans.—Between **N.E.** nearly and **S.S.E.**

8. *Q.*—You are heading **S.** and see a vessel's green light 2 points on your port bow; how must she be heading?

   Ans.—Between **N.N.W.** nearly and **S.W.**

Using the 000° to 360° notation

9. *Q.*—Your vessel is heading 040° C. and a vessel's red sidelight is seen 40° on your starboard bow; how is the observed vessel heading?

   Ans.—Between 260° C. nearly and 012° C.

10. *Q.*—You are heading 350° C. and see a vessel's green sidelight 30° on your port bow; how must she be heading?

    Ans.—Between 140° C. nearly and 028° C.

11. *Q.*—Your vessel is heading 135° C. when the starboard sidelight of a vessel is seen 35° on your port bow; how must the observed vessel be heading?
Ans.—Between 280° C. nearly and 168° C.

12. *Q.*—Your vessel is heading 220° C. and 45° on your starboard bow is seen the port side light of a vessel; how must the observed vessel be heading?
Ans.—Between 085° C. nearly and 197° C.

13. *Q.*—When heading 090° C. a vessel's green sidelight is seen 50° on your port bow; how is the observed vessel heading?
Ans.—Between 220° C. nearly and 108° C.

14. *Q.*—Your course is 280° C. when a vessel's red sidelight is seen 25° on your starboard bow; how is the vessel showing the red light heading?
Ans.—Between 125° C. nearly and 237° C.

The remaining questions are based on the same principle:—
You are required to state how a vessel was heading at the moment her coloured light disappeared.

RULE—The point on which she was heading was the 10th point from the *reversed bearing* of the light; for the inference is that she has just brought you a little more than 2 points abaft her beam.

15. *Q.*—You are heading N. and a red light disappears right ahead; how was the vessel showing its heading at the time?
Ans.—W.N.W.

16. *Q.*—You are heading S. and a green light disappears 2 points on your port bow; how was the vessel heading?
Ans.—S.W.

47. *Q.*—You are heading **E.** and a red light disappears 4 points
on your starboard bow; how was the vessel heading?
Ans.—**E.N.E.**

18. *Q.*—You are heading **W.** and a green light disappears
3 points on your port bow; how was the vessel heading?
Ans.—**N.W.** by **W.**

THE RULE OF THE ROAD AT SEA
POWER-DRIVEN VESSEL

Illustrated by Diagram

It is now presumed the reader has thoroughly mastered the Regulations for Preventing Collisions at Sea; that he can determine the approximate direction in which a vessel is heading on observing one of her sidelights, and is therefore in a position to reason out the correct action to take on meeting another vessel.

The following diagrams are inserted to illustrate different cases that may arise. In the diagrams, a number of vessels are shown, but it is to be distinctly understood that when each case is being considered only the vessel concerned is assumed to be in sight.

The key in each case indicates the action to be taken by the vessel in the centre of the diagram, with respect to the correspondingly numbered vessels.

Candidates are strongly advised, when studying the Rule of the Road, to avoid trying to commit the position of the light, or vessel, with its answer to memory from these diagrams. It is far better practice to try to understand in the case of a power-driven vessel the correct action necessary, i.e. whether to stand on or keep clear, and to be able to quote the correct Rule under which your decision is made. Where diagrams relating to sailing vessels are concerned, try to understand how the other vessel has the wind, then apply the rules given in Rule 12.

The term '*Stand on*' indicates that the vessel in the centre of the diagram, by virtue of her position relative to the other

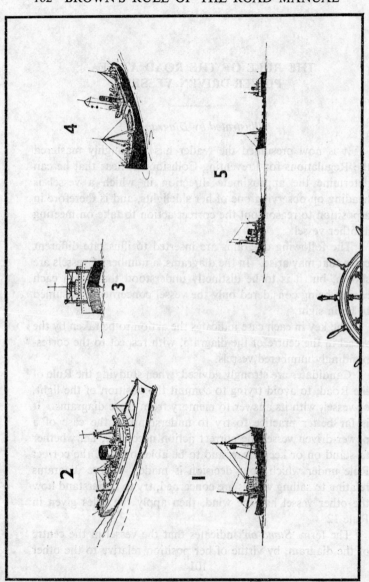

Diagram No. 2

Drawn by Hugh Lauder

vessel, must keep her course and speed, bearing in mind always the instructions given in Rule 17.

'*Keep clear*' signifies that the vessel in the centre of the diagram must keep out of the way of the other vessel. It does not indicate whether the course is to be altered to starboard or to port.

Key to Diagram No. 2

Important—In cases 1, 2 and 5, it is assumed there is no appreciable alteration in the bearing.

1. Keep clear, sailing trawler engaged in trawling. Alter course to port so as to pass well astern and give two short blasts on the whistle. (Rules 18 and 34.)

2. Stand on. On the other vessel's starboard side. (Rule 15.)

3. Meeting power-driven vessel end on. Alter course to starboard and sound one short blast on the whistle. (Rules 14 and 34.)

4. Keep clear, power-driven vessel not under command. (Rule 18 (*a*).

   Note—It would depend upon the movement of the vessel not under command whether alteration of course was necessary or not.

5. Keep clear. Tug with tow on the starboard bow. Alter course to starboard and sound one short blast on the whistle. (Rules 15, 18 and 34.)

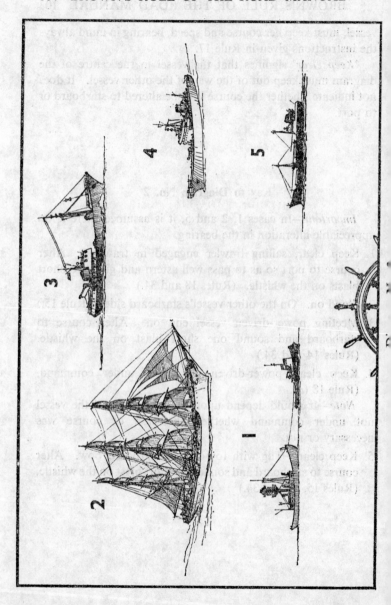

Key to Diagram No. 3

Important—In cases 1, 2, 4 and 5, it is assumed there is no appreciable alteration in the bearing

1. Keep clear, tug towing. (Rule 18.)
2. Keep clear. Sailing vessel crossing. Alter course to port and give two short blasts on the whistle. (Rules 18 and 34.)
3. *Keep clear*, if necessary. Power-driven trawler engaged in trawling. (Rule 18.)

   Note—The trawler is directly ahead and it may not be necessary to alter course to keep out of the way. If, however, alteration of course is necessary owing to the closeness of trawler, alter course to port, to pass well astern and not foul her trawl warp, and give two short blasts on the whistle.
4. Keep clear, vessel engaged laying or picking up a submarine cable or navigation mark, or in surveying or underwater operations. Alter course to starboard and give one short blast on the whistle. (Rules 18 and 34.)
5. Keep clear, power-driven vessel crossing and on the starboard bow. Alter course to starboard and give one short blast on the whistle. (Rules 15 and 34.)

QUESTIONS ON THE RULE OF THE ROAD
RELATING TO POWER-DRIVEN VESSELS

1. Heading north you see both sidelights and masthead lights of a power-driven vessel bearing **N.E.** and at the same time both sidelights and masthead lights of another power-driven vessel bearing **N.W.** What action would you take?

2. There is a power-driven vessel directly ahead, end on, and a tug with tow, heading to cross your course, about 2 points on your starboard bow. State how you would manoeuvre your vessel.

3. You observe a green light under a white light about 3 points on your port quarter. What would you do?

4. What would you do if thick fog set in when you were in charge of the bridge?

5. In thick fog, you are going along at a moderate speed sounding one prolonged blast on the whistle at intervals of 2 minutes and you hear a prolonged blast of the whistle of a power-driven vessel which is apparently forward of your beam. State what you would do under these circumstances.

6. In fog and at anchor your vessel is ringing the bell rapidly and sounding a gong at intervals of not less than one minute while a vessel is gradually approaching you giving one prolonged blast on her whistle. What action would you take?

7. In fog, proceeding at a moderate speed giving the Regulation fog signal, you hear a bell being rung rapidly for about 5 seconds every minute followed by one short, one

106

prolonged and one short blast on the whistle. Indicate what should be done under these circumstances.

8. There is a tug with tow showing her green light on your port bow, and a little nearer on your port bow the green light of a power-driven vessel. What alteration of course, if any, would you make?

9. Crossing from your port to starboard bow, there is a power-driven trawler with two cones, points together, suspended from the truck of her foremast. What action would you take?

10. You see the green sidelight of a sailing vessel to starboard and the port sidelight of a power-driven vessel to port. Would you, or would you not, alter course?

11. There is a power-driven vessel showing her green light about 2 points on your starboard bow, and 4 points on your port bow the green light of a sailing vessel is seen. How would you manoeuvre your vessel!

12. Approaching end on, there is a sailing vessel under fore and aft sail with a black conical shape, point downwards, suspended from her yard and about 2 points on your starboard bow there is a sailing trawler engaged in trawling. If the latter vessel is heading to cross your bow, what action would you take?

13. There is a power-driven vessel showing her red sidelight about 5 points on your starboard bow. What would you do in this case?

14. During falling snow when proceeding at a safe speed and making the Regulation fog signal, a vessel is detected ahead by radar range 2 miles. What action would you take?

15. Suppose you saw a white light ahead of you, what would it denote?

16. You see both sidelights of a sailing vessel right ahead. What alteration of course would you make?

17. There is a power-driven vessel ahead showing both side-lights and her masthead lights. About 4 points on the starboard bow there is a sailing vessel showing both her sidelights. The wind is 6 points on your port bow. How would you manoeuvre your vessel?

18. The wind is aft and you observe both sidelights of a sailing vessel directly ahead. What alteration of course would you make?

19. In fog, and having rung STOP on the engine-room tele-graph, what fog signal would you sound on the whistle?

20. What is meant by the expression 'a power-driven vessel under way but stopped and making no way through the water'?

21. When a power-driven trawler is engaged trawling, must she exhibit sidelights as well as her green and white lights?

22. Is there any right of way between two power-driven vessels in fog and not in sight of each other?

23. There is a fog bank directly ahead. What precaution should be taken before entering the fog?

24. In fog, a vessel fishing at anchor. What fog signal must she give?

ANSWERS

1. Keep clear of vessel bearing N.E. by maintaining course and speed.

2. Since it is necessary to keep clear of both vessels, alter course to starboard so as to pass astern of the *tow*, and give one short blast on the whistle.

3. Maintain course and speed, the observed vessel is an overtaking vessel.   See that the stern light is burning brightly.

4. Reduce down to a moderate speed and sound one prolonged blast on the whistle at intervals of not more than 2 minutes.   Send a messenger to inform the master of the weather conditions.

Note—The last sentence does not apply to those being examined for a Master's Certificate.

5. Stop the engines and navigate with caution until danger of collision is over.

Note—Two prolonged blasts must not be made on the whistle until the way is off the vessel.

6. Keep ringing the bell and sounding the gong and at a suitable moment after the other vessel's signal sound 'R' (short-long-short blasts in succession) on the whistle.

7. The signal heard indicates a vessel of 100 m., or less, in length is at anchor in the vicinity giving warning of her position.   Stop the engines, then navigate with caution.

8. Stand on for the power-driven vessel then keep out of the way of the tug which is restricted in ability to manoeuvre.

9. Alter course to port so as to pass well astern of the trawler which is engaged trawling, and sound two short blasts on the whistle.

10. No alteration of course is necessary as both are passing vessels and not crossing vessels.

11. Alter course to port, so as to pass astern of the sailing vessel and sound two short blasts on the whistle.

H

12. Keep clear of both vessels. Give one short blast on the whistle and alter course to starboard so as to pass well astern of the sailing trawler.

13. Keep clear if necessary. Carefully watch the bearing of the vessel. If the bearing does not appreciably change, make one short blast on the whistle and alter course to starboard so as to pass astern of the converging vessel.

14. Stop the ship and assess the situation by radar observation, sound the two-prolonged blasts fog signal until risk of collision is over.

15. It would indicate the presence of one of the following:—
    (i) Stern light of a vessel being overtaken.
    (ii) An approaching power-driven vessel under 50 metres in length.
    (iii) Vessel under 50 metres in length at anchor.
    (iv) A vessel under oars.
    (v) A sailing vessel under 7 metres.
    (vi) A seaplane at anchor.

16. Alter course to starboard or port, whichever is most convenient, preferably to windward and make the requisite signal on the whistle in accordance with Rule 34.

17. Give one short blast on the whistle and alter course to starboard in order to clear the power-driven vessel. Maintaining this course and speed will clear the sailing vessel.

18. The sailing vessel is in stays. Note which tack she pays off on, then alter course to pass astern, giving the necessary signal on the whistle in accordance with Rule 34. If the sailing vessel shuts out her red light, she is standing away on the starboard tack; if the green light is shut out she is standing away on the port tack.

19. One prolonged blast at intervals of not more than 2 minutes until the way is off the vessel, then two prolonged blasts at intervals of not more than 2 minutes.

20. That the motive power is not being used to move the vessel through the water, hence, she would not alter the bearing or distance of an unattached floating object.

21. Yes, also a stern light.

22. No right of way exists when the vessels are not in sight of each other.

23. Before entering the fog, ease down to a safe speed and sound one prolonged blast on the whistle at intervals of not more than 2 minutes.

24. Sound, at intervals of not more than 2 minutes, three blasts in succession, namely, one prolonged blast followed by two short blasts.

TO DETERMINE THE DIRECTION IN WHICH
A SAILING VESSEL IS HEADING

The motive power of a sailing vessel is provided by Nature
in the form of wind which, pressing on sails set to the best
advantage, causes her to forge ahead.

The direction in which a sailing vessel may proceed is
governed by the direction of the wind. In the case of a
square-rigged vessel, the nearest she can lie to the wind and
still make headway is from 6 to 6½ points—in strong winds
7 points; she is then close-hauled. Fore and aft rigged vessels
can approach nearer than 6 points from the 'Wind's eye'.
Some may lie about 4 points from the wind, but this depends
upon the design of the vessel and her sail plan. As a rule
6 points is generally taken as the nearest approach to the
direction of the wind when ascertaining the possible direction
in which a sailing vessel can be heading on observing one of
her sidelights.

To find the direction in which a sailing vessel is heading,
proceed as follows:—

Take a bearing of the light.

Reverse the bearing and calculate 10 points to the right or
left of the reversed bearing, for red and green light respectively,
as in the case of a power-driven vessel, but in ascertaining the
possible direction of the ship's head only reckon those points
which are included *between the reversed bearing and the 6th
point from the wind.*

Note—In the examples given in this book, no account is
taken of the aberration of the wind due to the movement of
the vessel through the water.

Example—A sailing vessel *A*, close-hauled on the starboard tack heading North, observes the green sidelight of a sailing

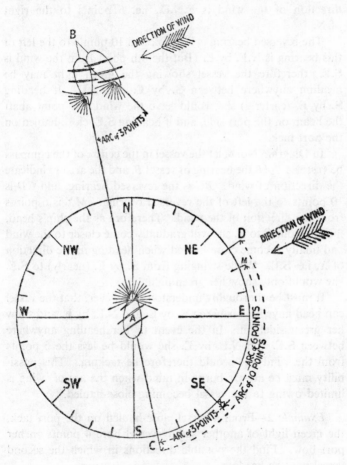

Diagram No. 4

vessel *B* bearing **N. by W.** Find the possible directions which the second vessel may be heading.

Since *A* close-hauled to starboard and heading **N.**, the direction of the wind is **E.N.E.**, i.e. 6 points to the right of **N.**

The reversed bearing is **S. by E.** and 10 points to the left of this bearing is **N.E. by E.** But the 6th point from the wind is **S.E.**, therefore the vessel showing the green light may be heading anywhere between **S. by E.** and **S.E.** If heading **S. by E.** (easterly) she would have the wind one point abaft the beam on the port side, and if heading **S.E.** close-hauled on the port tack.

In Diagram No. 4, let the vessel in the centre of the compass be vessel *A*. *AB* the bearing of vessel *B*, and the arrows indicate the direction of wind. *BC* is the reversed bearing, and *CD* is 10 points to the left of the reversed bearing. *MX* is 6 points from the direction of the wind. Therefore as the ship's head, moved from *C* to *X*, she will gradually come closer to the wind and finally become close-hauled when heading in the direction of *X*, i.e. **S.E.** While swinging from **S. by E.** (nearly) to **S.E.** she would only show her green light.

It must be thoroughly understood, however, that the vessel can head anywhere between **S. by E.** and **N.E. by E.** and show her green sidelight. In the event of her heading anywhere between **S.E.** and **N.E. by E.** she would be less the 6 points from the wind and would therefore be tacking. This possibility must be always borne in mind when the arc of swing is limited owing to the vessel becoming close-hauled.

Example 2—From a vessel close-hauled on the port tack, the green light of another sailing vessel bore 4 points on her port bow. Find the possible directions in which the second vessel may be heading.

The reversed bearing is 4 points on the starboard quarter. Ten points to the left of the reversed bearing gives 2 points on the starboard bow.   Now 4 points on the starboard quarter

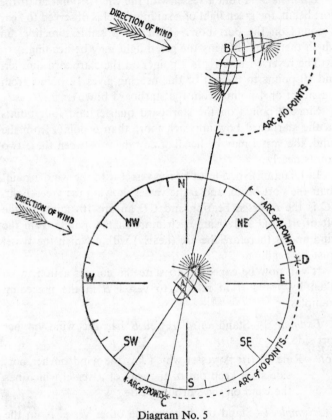

Diagram No. 5

is 14 points from the direction of the wind, and swinging to the left goes further from the wind, therefore the second vessel may be heading anywhere from nearly 4 points on the observing vessel's starboard quarter to 2 points on her starboard bow.

Example 3—From a vessel with the wind 1 point abaft the port beam, the green light of a sailing vessel is observed to bear 2 points on the port bow. Find the possible directions in which the vessel showing the green light may be heading.

The reversed bearing is 2 points on the starboard quarter, and 10 points to the left of this bearing gives 12 points from the stern, or 4 points from the starboard bow.

Since 2 points on the starboard quarter and four points on the starboard bow are each more than 6 points from the wind, the vessel may be heading anywhere between these two points nearly.

In Diagram No. 5 let *A* be the vessel with the wind 1 point abaft the port beam, and *B* the vessel showing the green light. *BC* is the reversed bearing and *CD* an arc 10 points to the left of *BC*. *C* and *D* are each more than 6 points from the wind and is therefore the arc (nearly) within which the vessel must be heading.

It will now be expedient to state the correct action to be taken by vessel *A* in respect to vessel *B* in the preceding examples.

Example 1—Stand on. Vessel *B* has the wind on her port side.

Note—Rule 12 (i): A vessel which has the wind on her port side shall keep out of the way of a vessel which has the wind on the starboard side.

Example 2—Stand on, because the other vessel is on the same tack and is to windward. She must keep out of the way by Rule 12 (ii).

Example 3—Keep clear. The vessel with the wind on the

port side must keep out of the way of the vessel with the wind on the starboard side.

1. *Q.*—You are heading **N.** with the wind right aft and see a sailing ship's red light 4 points on your starboard bow; how must she be heading?
   Ans.—Between **W.S.W.** and **N.N.W.**

2. *Q.*—You are heading **N.** with the wind right aft and see a sailing ship's green light 2 points on your port bow; how must she be heading?
   Ans.—Between **E.S.E.** and **N.E.**

3. *Q.*—You are heading **N.** with the wind right aft and see a sailing ship's red light 2 points on your starboard bow; how must she be heading?
   Ans.—Between **W.S.W.** and **N.W.**

4. *Q.*—You are heading **N.** with the wind right aft and see a sailing ship's green light 4 points on your port bow; how must she be heading?
   Ans.—Between **E.S.E.** and **N.N.E.**

5. *Q.*—You are heading **S.** with the wind **N.** and see a sailing ship's red light 4 points on your starboard bow; how must she be heading?
   Ans.—Between **E.N.E.** and **S.S.E.**

6. *Q.*—You are heading **S.** with the wind **N.** and see a sailing ship's green light 2 points on your port bow; how must she be heading?
   Ans.—Between **W.N.W.** and **S.W.**

7. *Q.*—You are heading **S.** with the wind **N.** and see a sailing ship's red light 2 points on your starboard bow; how must she be heading?
   Ans.—Between **E.N.E.** and **S.E.**

8. You are heading **S.** with the wind right aft and see a
sailing ship's green light 4 points on your port bow;
how must she be heading?
Ans.—Between **W.N.W.** and **S.S.W.**

9. *Q.*—You are heading **N.** and are close-hauled to port and
see a sailing ship's red light 2 points on your starboard
bow; how must she be heading?
Ans.—Between **S.S.W.** and **S.W.**

10. *Q.*—You are heading **N.** with the wind abeam on your
port side, and see a sailing ship's red light 1 point on
your starboard bow; how must she be heading?
Ans.—Between **S. by W.** to **S.S.W.**

11. *Q.*—You are heading **N.** with the wind 2 points abaft the
port beam, and see a sailing ship's red light 3 points
on your starboard bow; how must she be heading?
Ans.—Between **N.W. by N.** and **N.W.**

12. *Q.*—You are heading **N.** with the wind on the port
quarter, and see a sailing ship's red light 2 points on
your starboard bow; how must she be heading?
Ans.—Between **N.W.** and **W.N.W.**

13. *Q.*—You are heading **N.** with the wind on the starboard
quarter, and see a sailing ship's green light 1 point on
your port bow; how must she be heading?
Ans.—Between **N.E. by E.** and **E.N.E.**

14. *Q.*—You are heading **N.** with the wind 2 points abaft the
starboard beam, and see a sailing ship's green light
2 points on your port bow; how must she be heading?
Ans.—**N.E.** only.

15. *Q.*—You are heading **N.** with the wind abeam on your

starboard side, and see a sailing ship's green light
4 points on your port bow; how must she be heading?
Ans.—**N.N.E.** only.

16. *Q.*—You are heading **N.** and are close-hauled on the
starboard tack, and see a sailing ship's green light
2 points on your port bow; how must she be heading?
Ans.—Between **S.S.E.** and **S.E.**

TERMS ASSOCIATED WITH SAILING VESSELS

Starboard tack	Sailing close to the wind with it blowing against the starboard side. The tacks of the courses (lower sails) being boarded.
Port tack	Sailing close to the wind with it blowing against the port side. The tacks of the courses being boarded.
Close-hauled *By the wind* *Tacking*	Sailing as close to the wind as possible.
Staying *Going about*	Changing from one tack to the other by bringing the ship's head into the wind.
Wearing *Wind abeam*	Changing from one tack to the other by bringing the wind astern.
Beam wind	Sailing with the wind directly abeam.
Going free *Running* *Off the wind*	Sailing with wind abeam or on the quarter.
Before the wind	Sailing with the wind aft.
Luff	To bring the ship's head nearer to the wind.
Keep away	To turn the ship's head away from the wind.
Lying to	Keeping the ship's head to the wind with small sail in a gale.
Hove to	Keeping the ship stationary by trimming sail so that one acts against the other.
Backing and *filling*	Sailing forwards and backwards across a river and letting the tide take the ship to windward.

THE RULE OF THE ROAD AT SEA
SAILING VESSEL

Diagram 6

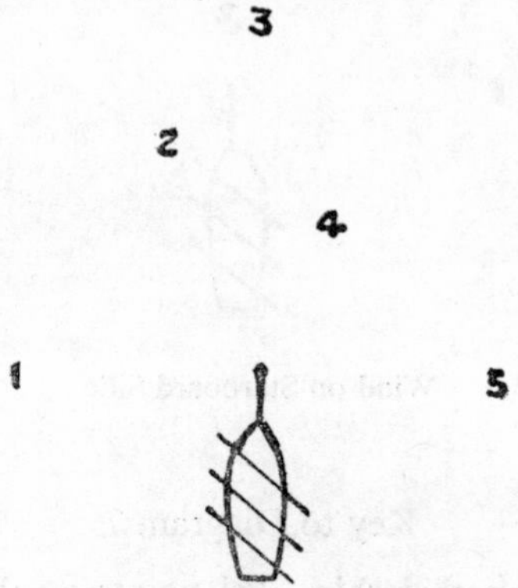

3

2

4

1   **5**

Wind on Port Side

Key to Diagram 6

1. Stand on, lee ship.
2. Keep clear, she may be free to starboard. (One point on the weather bow, she can be 9 points from the wind on the starboard side or 13 points from it on the port side.)
3. Keep clear, she has the wind abeam on the starboard side.
4. Keep clear, she may be close-hauled on the starboard tack. (One point on the lee bow, she could be 7 points from the wind on the starboard side, or 3 points from it on the port side.)
5. Keep clear, weather ship.

Diagram 7

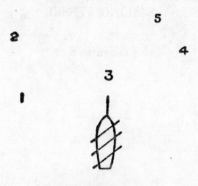

Wind on Starboard Side

Key to Diagram 7

1. Keep clear, weather ship. (6½ points on the lee bow.)
2. Keep clear, weather ship (4 points on the lee bow, she would lay 4 points from the wind on the port side, or 6 points from the wind on the starboard side).
3. Stand on, she is on the port tack. (Right ahead she is 8 points from the wind.)
4. Stand on, she may be free to port or on starboard tack to windward.
5. Stand on. There is no risk of collision.

QUESTIONS ON THE RULE OF THE ROAD RELATING TO SAILING VESSELS

1. Sailing close-hauled on the starboard tack, you observe the red sidelight of a power-driven vessel on your starboard bow, and both sidelights of a sailing vessel directly ahead. Would you, or would you not, alter course?

2. Sailing with the wind 2 points abaft the beam on the starboard side, both sidelights of a sailing vessel are observed directly ahead at the same time as the port sidelight of a power-driven vessel is seen 4 points on the starboard bow. Would you, or would you not, alter course?

3. Running with the wind dead aft, the green and red sidelights of a sailing vessel are seen directly ahead at the same instant as the starboard light of another sailing vessel is seen 3 points on the port bow. What action would you take?

4. When close-hauled on the port tack a tug with tow heading to cross your course bears 3 points on the port bow and a steam vessel is approaching end on. Would you make any alteration in your course?

5. When heading east with the wind free to starboard and overhauling a power-driven vessel steering east, a tug with tow steering about north bears 2 points on the starboard bow. What action would you take?

6. Logging 6 knots with the wind abeam on the port side, you observe directly ahead a power-driven vessel with two black balls hoisted. What would you do?

7. Sailing with the wind on the port quarter a vessel showing

123

bow, while 2 points on the same bow a vessel showing two red lights over a green light is heading across your course. What action would you take under these circumstances? a green light over a white light is seen 1 point on the port

8. When on the starboard tack, a trawler with cones, points together is seen 2 points on the starboard bow. If the trawler is steering to cross your bow, would you 'stand on' or 'keep out of the way'?

9. When is a sailing vessel said to be on the starboard tack?

10. What fog signal should be given by a sailing vessel when becalmed in a dense fog with no steering way upon her and yards trimmed square?

11. During dense fog the sound signal, one long blast followed by two short blasts, is heard. What does this indicate?

12. What vessels are regarded as restricted in their ability to manoeuvre?

13. What are the responsibilities between a sailing vessel underway and a vessel (a) Not under command; (b) Restricted in her ability to manoeuvre; (c) Engaged in fishing?

14. What shapes are exhibited by a dredger at anchor when an obstruction exists?

15. When the size of a vessel engaged in diving makes it impracticable to exhibit the prescribed shapes, what does she exhibit?

ANSWERS

1. No. Maintain course and speed. The power-driven vessel will keep out of the way and since the sailing vessel must be on port tack she also will keep out of the way.

2. No, the sailing vessel is on the port tack and the power-driven vessel will also keep clear.

3. The vessel ahead is in stays while the vessel on the bow may be close-hauled to starboard. Keep clear of both vessels, Weather Ship.

4. No alteration of course is necessary, both vessels will keep clear.

5. Alter course to keep clear of the power-driven vessel being overhauled. Stand on for the tug.

6. Keep clear, the vessel is not under command.

7. The vessel, 1 point on the port bow, is a power-driven trawler engaged in trawling. The other vessel on the port bow is not under command but making way through the water. Alter course to pass astern of the vessel not under command, and so by doing keep clear of the trawler.

8. Keep out of the way. [Rule 18 (b).]

9. When sailing with the wind on her starboard side so that the mainsail is carried on the port side. [Rule 12 (b).]

10. One long blast followed by two short blasts at intervals of not more than 2 minutes.

11. A vessel:—Not under command; restricted in ability to manoeuvre; Towing: Fishing or a Sailing vessel.

12. Vessels engaged in:—Laying, servicing or picking up a navigation mark, submarine cable or pipeline; transferring persons or cargo while underway; launching or recovering aircraft; minesweeping; towing when a deviation from her course is restricted.

13. The sailing vessel must keep clear.

14. Shapes in a vertical line where they can best be seen, ball, diamond, ball; and in addition placed lower than the

three shapes and not less than 2 metres horizontal
distance from them, two balls in a vertical line indicating
the obstructed side and two diamonds vertically to
indicate the side a vessel may pass.

15. A rigid replica of the International Code Flag 'A'.

INTERNATIONAL ASSOCIATION OF LIGHTHOUSE AUTHORITIES (IALA)
MARITIME BUOYAGE SYSTEM 'A'
Combined Cardinal and Lateral System (Red to Port)
ADOPTED BY THE GENERAL LIGHTHOUSE AUTHORITIES OF THE UNITED KINGDOM

In narrow channels, rivers and approaches to harbours which are frequently strewn with hidden dangers, such as rocks, shoals, wrecks, etc., aids to navigation are provided in the form of buoyage marks. System 'A' applies to all fixed and floating marks except lighthouses, sector lights, leading lights and marks, lightships and 'lighthouse buoys'.

TYPES OF MARKS

(1) **Lateral Marks** indicate the port and starboard sides of channels.

(2) **Cardinal Marks** indicate that navigable water lies to the North, South, East or West by compass from the mark.

(3) **Safe Water Marks** indicate that navigable water lies all round. The mark may be used as a centre-line, mid-channel or landfall buoy.

(4) **Isolated Danger Mark** is erected on or moored above a danger of limited extent which has navigable water all round it.

(5) **Special Marks** indicate a special area or feature shown on a chart, including Traffic Separation marks, Spoil Ground marks, Military Exercise Zone, Cable or Pipe Line marks, Ocean Data Acquisition Systems (ODAS) buoys carrying oceanographic or meteorological sensors. Special Buoys may be used to mark the boundaries of a deep-water channel within a wide estuary channel.

SHAPES OF MARKS

There are five basic shapes of buoys, namely 'CAN', 'CONICAL', 'SPHERICAL', 'PILLAR' and SPAR'. The term 'Pillar' is used to describe any buoy which is smaller than a 'Lighthouse Buoy' and which has a tall vertical structure on a broad base.

There are four types of topmarks used in system 'A', namely 'Can', 'Conical', 'Spherical' and 'X-shaped'. The top marks on Pillar and on Spar Buoys are very important, and they will always be fitted wherever practicable.

MARKING SIDES OF CHANNELS

Port-hand Marks.

Shape: Can, Pillar or Spar.

Colour: All RED.

Topmark: (if any) Red Can (always fitted on Pillar and Spar buoys).

Light: (if any) *Red* light, any rhythm may be used (flashing, occulting, isophase, quick flashing, long flashing, group flashing).

Starboard-hand Marks.

Shape: Conical, Pillar or Spar.

Colour: All GREEN.

Topmark: (if any) Green Cone, point up (always fitted on Pillar and Spar buoys).

Light: (if any) *Green* light, any rhythm may be used (e.g.:— quick flashing, long flashing, group flashing.)

Definition of the words 'Starboard Hand and Port Hand'

The term 'Starboard Hand' shall denote that side which would be on the right hand of the mariner when approaching a harbour, river, estuary or other waterway from seaward; the term 'Port Hand' shall denote the left hand of the mariner under the same circumstances.

In other areas, the general direction of buoyage is determined by following a clockwise route around continental land masses given in Sailing Directions and, if necessary, indicated on charts by a broad arrow symbol:—

Around the British Isles the general direction of lateral buoyage runs Northwards along the West coasts and through the Irish Sea, Eastwards through the English Channel and Northwards through the North Sea, from Orfordness to the Shetland Isles.

Variations on Lateral System

In some places, such as straits which are open at both ends, the local direction of buoyage may be over-ridden by the general direction. In some countries other than the United Kingdom, Starboard hand marks may be coloured *black*, instead of green, in exceptional cases.

Beacons marking the sides of channels have the same topmark shapes and colours as those used by the Can and the Conical buoys.

In cases where *red* or *green* lights are used to indicate pierheads or jetties, they are shown in pairs, namely two fixed *red* lights, one above the other and two fixed *green* lights, one above the other. If single *red* or *green* lights are used, they will be flashing or occulting to avoid confusion with the navigation lights of ships in the vicinity.

Special Types of Channel Marking

In a wide estuary where the channel for normal navigation is marked by red Can and green Conical buoys it may be necessary to indicate a special channel for deep draught vessels, and this is done by Special Marks. The buoys are coloured *Yellow*, shaped Can, Conical or Spherical and when a topmark is carried it is a single yellow 'X' (multiplication cross). When a light is exhibited it is *yellow*, any rhythm, except those used for the *white* lights of Cardinal, Isolated Danger and Safe Water Marks.

CARDINAL MARKS

A Cardinal mark indicates the direction by compass away from the mark where the mariner may find the best navigable water. The buoys are shaped Pillar or Spar, and are placed in one of the *four quadrants of the compass* (North, East, South or West), bounded by the true bearings NW–NE, NE–S E SE–SW, SW–NW taken *from the buoy*.

A Cardinal buoy is named:—

> North when the safe area is N. of the North buoy
> South when the safe area is S. of the South buoy
> East when the safe area is E. of the East buoy
> West when the safe area is W. of the West buoy

The Cardinal marks may be used to indicate the deepest water in an area; the safe side on which to pass a danger, or to draw attention to a bend, a junction, or the end of a shoal in a channel.

The mariner must memorise the characteristics of the four Cardinal buoys so that the correct action is taken at once, especially if a buoy is sighted unexpectedly in poor visibility, which buoy may be marking a new uncharted danger, such as a wreck.

Cardinal buoys are painted Black and Yellow in horizontal bands, and the most important feature to remember by day is the arrangement of **Black double-cone topmarks.** The cones are as large as possible and clearly separated. The position of the black band on the buoy is related to the points of the black topmark, as follows:

Topmark Cones	Buoy Colour
North Points UP ▲	Black band *above* yellow band
South Points DOWN ▼	Black band *below* yellow band
East Points OUTWARD ◆	Black bands *above and below* yellow band
West Points INWARD ⧗	Black band with yellow *above and below*

(Aid to remember West topmark—'W for Wineglass'.)

At night a cardinal buoy is distinguished by a Quick Flashing (Qk Fl) or a Very Quick Flashing (V Qk Fl) *White* light and the safe quadrant is indicated by groups of flashes:—

NORTH BUOY—Uninterrupted quick or very quick flashes

EAST BUOY—3 flashes in a group

SOUTH BUOY—6 flashes in a group immediately followed by a long flash

WEST BUOY—9 flashes in a group

An aid to remember the group flashes is to think of the face of a clock then:

3 flashes—3 o'clock—East mark

6 flashes—6 o'clock—South mark

9 flashes—9 o clock—West mark

The long flash of not less than 2 seconds follows the 6 flashes to avoid mistaking it for 3 or 9 flashes.

The rate of flashing is 60 or 50 per minute for quick flashing and 120 or 100 per minute for very quick flashing.

The periods of the East, South and West lights are 10 seconds 15 seconds, and 15 seconds when quick flashing or the periods are every 5 seconds 10 seconds, and 10 seconds when very quick flashing lights are used. A choice of the rate of flashing is required in case two North buoys are placed near each other and confusion must be avoided.

Isolated Danger Marks

The Isolated danger mark is used to indicate the position of a dangerous rock, or an islet separated by a narrow channel from the coast, or a shoal which may be well off shore and have navigable water all round it. The mark may be erected on the danger or a Pillar or a Spar buoy moored above it. The buoy is coloured *black* with one or more *red horizontal bands*, and carries a *topmark* consisting of *two large black spheres* clearly separated in a vertical line. A lighted isolated danger buoy shows *white flashes* in groups of *two flashes*.

Safe Water Marks

A safe water buoy is used as a landfall mark or a centre-line or a mid-channel mark having navigable water all round it. It is shaped Spherical, Pillar or Spar and coloured *red-and-white vertical stripes*. A *topmark* consisting of *a single red sphere* is carried except on the spherical-shaped buoy. A lighted safe water buoy shows *one long white flash* every 10 seconds or may show a white light, occulting or isophase.

New Dangers

A new danger to navigation is defined as a newly-discovered hazard not yet shown on charts or sailing directions, or sufficiently promulgated by Notices to Mariners.

A New Danger is marked by one or more Cardinal or Lateral buoys in accordance with the System 'A' rules. If the danger is especially grave, at least one of the marks will be duplicated as soon as possible by an identical mark until the danger has been sufficiently promulgated. The duplicate mark may carry a racon, coded W (. — —), showing a signal length of one nautical mile on a radar display. If the new danger is marked by a Cardinal buoy it must show a *quick flashing or very quick flashing White light*; if marked by a Lateral buoy, it must show a *quick flashing or very quick flashing Red or Green* light.

QUESTIONS ON THE BUOYAGE SYSTEM 'A'

1. Describe the shape and colour of a starboard-hand lateral mark.

2. May the marks denoting the sides of a channel carry top-marks? and if so describe them.

3. What lights may be shown by buoys marking the sides of a channel?

4. Describe the shape, colour and top-mark of a North cardinal buoy.

5. How would you recognise a North cardinal buoy at night?

6. On which side would you pass a safe water mark in a channel?

7. Describe an isolated danger mark.

8. What is a middle ground?

9. Would you expect the channels on each side of a middle ground to be of equal importance?

10. How is a channel for deep draught vessels marked in a wide estuary?

11. Can buoys be relied upon to maintain their correct position?

12. How would you distinguish between a moored buoy and a buoy adrift?

13. Describe the top-mark and light on an East cardinal buoy.

14. When heading North a buoy is sighted ahead showing two black cones, points inward. What alteration of your course is necessary?

15. Describe a spoil ground buoy.

16. How may a dangerous wreck be marked?

17. What is the Local Direction of Lateral buoyage?

18. What is the General Direction of buoyage around the British Isles?

19. How is the general direction of buoyage determined in other areas?

20. What type of special buoy may be sighted in mid-ocean?

ANSWERS

1. Starboard hand marks are Conical-, Pillar- or Spar-shaped, coloured green. (In exceptional cases black may be used; but not in the United Kingdom.)

2. Yes, the marks on the sides of a channel may carry top-marks. These are:
   Starboard hand—a green Cone, point upwards
   Port hand—a red Can

3. Starboard hand—a flashing *green* light having any rhythm. Port hand—a flashing *red* light having any rhythm.
   The rhythm may be quick flashing, flashing, long flashing or group flashing.

4. A North cardinal buoy is Pillar- or Spar-shaped, coloured black above yellow and the top-mark shows two black cones, points upward.

5. A North cardinal buoy shows quick or very quick uninterrupted *white* flashes.

6. The safe water mark may be passed on either hand, but should preferably be left to port.

7. The isolated danger mark is a Pillar or a Spar buoy painted black with one or more horizontal red bands. It carries a top mark of two large black spheres clearly separated vertically and when lighted, shows a *white* light group flashing two.

8. A middle ground is a shoal in a river, estuary or approach to a harbour, with a channel on each side of it.

9. They may be of equal importance or the main channel may be to the right or to the left of the middle ground.

10. The deep channel is marked by Conical and Can special buoys, coloured yellow, and they mark the starboard and port sides of the deep channel. The top mark is a yellow 'X', and when lighted they show a *yellow* occulting or isophase light. The centre line of the channel may be marked by yellow spherical special buoys.

11. No. They may get out of position on account of gales, and should be regarded as warnings only.

12. A buoy adrift would float with its weed-line above water level.

13. The East cardinal buoy has a top mark of two black cones, points outward, and when lighted, gives 3 *white* flashes. The rhythm is 3 very quick flashes every 5 seconds or 3 quick flashes every 10 seconds.

14. The inward-pointing cones indicate a West cardinal buoy, and the safe side to pass the buoy is to the west of it. Alter course to port.

15. Spoil ground is marked by a special buoy, spherical in shape, and top mark 'X' all coloured yellow. A flashing *yellow* light may be shown.

16. A wreck is marked by one or more Cardinal or Lateral buoys in accordance with the System 'A' rules. The Cardinal buoys top marks and *white* quick flashing lights indicate the safe side to pass the wreck. If the Lateral green Conical and red Can buoys are used they give quick or very quick flashes of their respective *green* or *red* lights.

If the wreck is a gravé danger to shipping, one of the marks will be duplicated and a racon may be carried, coded 'W' (. — —).

17. The local direction of buoyage for lateral marks is the direction taken by the mariner when approaching a harbour, river estuary or other waterway from seaward.

18. The general direction of lateral buoyage around the British Isles runs Northward along the West coasts and through the Irish Sea, Eastward through the English Channel and Northward through the North Sea. The general direction gives way to the local direction at the outer limit of the Thames Estuary.

19. The direction of buoyage is determined by the buoyage authorities, following a clockwise direction around continental land masses given in the Sailing Directions and if necessary, indicated on charts by a broad arrow symbol.

20. A special buoy carrying instruments to collect information about weather and ocean movements, called an Ocean Data Acquisition System (ODAS) buoy.

INFORMATION RE FOG SIGNALS

The following information in regard to fog signals is promulgated for the guidance of mariners:—

(1) Fog signals are heard at greatly-varying distances.

(2) Under certain conditions of atmosphere, when an air fog signal is a combination of high and low tones, one of the notes may be inaudible.

(3) There are occasionally areas around a fog signal in which it is wholly inaudible.

(4) A fog may exist a short distance from a station and not be observable from it, so that the signal may not be sounded.

(5) Some fog signals cannot be started at a moment's notice after signs of fog have been observed.

Mariners are therefore warned that fog signals cannot be implicitly relied upon, and that *the practice of sounding should never be neglected*. Particular attention should be given to placing 'Look-out men' in positions in which the noises in the ship are least likely to interfere with the hearing of the sound of an air fog signal; as experience shows that, though such a signal may not be heard from the deck or bridge when the engines are moving, it may be heard when the ship is stopped, or from a quiet position. It may sometimes be heard from aloft, though not on deck.

There are three means adopted for signalling in fog:—

(a) By air sound signals comprising (1) *Diaphone*, (2) *Siren*, (3) *Reed*, (4) *Nautophone*, (5) *Electric Fog Horn*, (6) *Gun*, (7) *Explosive*, (8) *Bell* or *Gong*, and (9) *Whistle*.

(b) By submarine sound signals produced either by (10) an *Oscillator* or (11) *Bell*; and

(c) By Radio Telegraphy.

138

I. Air Fog Signals

The *Diaphone* (1), *Siren* (2), and *Reed* (3) are all three compressed air instruments fitted with horns for distributing the sound.

The *Diaphone* emits a powerful low-tone note terminating with sharp descending note termed the 'grunt', the *Siren* a medium-powered note, either high or low or a combination of the two, and the *Reed* a high note of less power. *Reeds* may be hand-operated, in which case the signals from them are of small power.

The *Nautophone* (4) is an electrically-operated instrument also fitted with a horn, and emits a high note signal similar in power and tone to that of the Reed.

The Electric Fog Horn (5) is an electrically-operated instrument consisting of emitters from each of which a number of sound frequencies are emitted simultaneously, producing a powerful, medium-pitched note.

Gun (6) and *Explosive* (7) signals are produced by the firing of explosives charges, the former being discharged from a gun and the latter being exploded in mid-air. An acetylene gun gives a brilliant flash at the time of the explosion.

Bells (8) may be operated either mechanically or by wave action, in which latter case the sound is irregular. The notes may be high, medium or low, according to the weight of the bell. *Gongs* are also sometimes employed.

A *Whistle* (9) is a signal produced by compressed air or steam, emitted through a slot in a circular chamber.

II. Submarine Sound Signals

The *Oscillator* (10) is an electrically-operated instrument sounding a high note signal.

Bells (11) may be operated either mechanically or by wave motion, in which latter case the sound is irregular.

The effective range of submarine sound signals far exceeds that of air sound signals, having been known to exceed 50 miles in the case of an oscillator and 15 miles in that of a bell. Their bearings can be determined with sufficient accuracy for safe navigation in a fog if a vessel is equipped with receivers, and even should a vessel be not so equipped, submarine signals may be heard from below the water line for distances which are well outside the range of air fog signals, though their bearings cannot then be so well determined.

NOTES ON SIDE-LIGHTS, MASTHEAD AND STERN LIGHTS

Oil Lights

1. *Side-Lights*: *Screening Abaft the Beam*—The wick or wicks of a side-light must be placed at an angle of $112\frac{1}{2}°$ with the fore-and-aft line of the ship; in other words, they must be parallel to the direction 2 points abaft the beam. The burner must be so placed that a line drawn in this direction from the after edge of the wick in the case of a single burner, and of the forward wick in the case of a duplex burner, shall cut the edge of the housing of the lens.

2. *Side-lights*: *Screening Forward*—The screens of side-lights, the length of which should never be less than 36 inches from the flame to the chock or its equivalent, must always be placed parallel to the line of the keel. The chocking must be so arranged to show a 'thwart ship value' of at least 1 inch of wick in a forward direction; that is to say, a person looking past the edge of the chock in a line parallel to the keel must be able to see at least 1 inch of wick.

3. *Masthead Lights*: *Screening*—In a masthead light the wick or wicks must be at right angles to the line of the keel,

and their setting must be such that lines drawn from the centre of the after edge of the wick in the case of a single burner, and of the forward wick in the case of a duplex burner, in directions 2 points abaft the beam on each side, shall cut the edges of the housing of the lens.

4. *Stern Lights Screening*—The wick of an oil stern lantern must be set as in the oil masthead lantern and so screened that a line drawn from the centre of the edge of the wick nearest the back of the lantern in a direction $67\frac{1}{2}°$ from right aft on either side shall cut the edge of the housing of the lens or plain glass front.

Electric Lights

5. *Voltage*—The voltage of the electric supply on board should preferably not be less than 110 or greater than 220 volts. The supply of electric current for navigation lights should be kept at its full voltage throughout the voyage, as under-running of the voltage may result in serious loss of candle-power.

6. *Candle Power*—As a general rule, 40-watt lamps, which will give a candle-power of approximately 32 candles, will be found satisfactory.

Type of Lamp—Lamps should be of the vacuum type, having the cylindrical 'squirrel cage' form of filament, and should conform to British Standard Specification No. 555 of 1939 for navigation lamps. Gas-filled lamps should not be used.

The diameter or width of the cage formed by the filament should not be less than one inch (*see* paragraph 9) and not greater than $1\frac{3}{8}$ inches.

7. *Position of Lamps*—In all electric lanterns fitted with dioptric lenses, and preferably in all other electric lanterns, the lamp should be fitted in an upright position (pip upwards).

In all electric lanterns fitted with dioptric lenses, the height of the socket should be so adjusted that the luminous centre

K

of the source of light coincides with the centre of the lens. Further, the luminous centre of the filament should always be the same distance above the cap of the lamp.

8. *Side-Lights   Screening   Abaft   the   Beam*—The lamp socket of an electric side lantern should be so placed that a line drawn in a direction two points abaft the beam, being a tangent to the forward half of a circle, $\frac{5}{8}$-inch diameter, concentric with the socket, will cut the edge of the housing of the lens or plain glass front.   The centre of the lamp socket should be placed $\frac{5}{16}$-inch abaft the centre from which the curvature of the lens or plain glass front is struck.

9. *Side-Lights Screening Forward*—The screen of a side lantern, whether oil or electric, must never be less than 36 inches in length from the flame (or filament if an electric lamp is used) to the chock or its equivalent, and must always be placed parallel to the line of the keel.   The chocking must be so arranged to show a 'thwart ship value' of at least one inch of wick (or filament) in a forward direction; that is to say a person looking past the edge of the chock in a line parallel to the keel must be able to see at least one inch of wick (or filament).

10. *Masthead Lights*: *Screening*—The lamp socket of an electric masthead lantern should be so placed that a line drawn in a direction $22\frac{1}{2}°$ abaft the beam on either side being a tangent to the forward half of a circle $\frac{5}{8}$-inch in diameter and concentric with the lamp socket, will cut the edge of the housing of the lens or plain glass front.   The centre of the lamp-socket should be $\frac{5}{16}$-inch abaft the centre from which the curvature of the lens or plain glass front is struck.

11. *Side-Lights*: *Construction and Position of Screens*—If the screen is made of wood, it should be well seasoned and not less than $1\frac{1}{4}$ inches in thickness.   If the screen is made of

steel, the chock should still be made of wood so that its width
may be adjusted, if necessary, during re-survey. The chock
should be rounded off. When the set screw of the cleat is
screwed hard up, the back of the lantern should fit closely
against the back of the screen, and the side of the lantern
should be parallel to the side of the screen.

Separate screens for oil and electric side-lights should
always, if practicable, be provided.

Screens are never to be secured to the rigging, except as
permitted in paragraph 12. If screens are attached to movable
davits or to outriggers extending outwards over the sides of
the ship, they should be fitted with stop pins or distance rods
so arranged that when the stop pins or distance rods are in
their places the screens will be parallel to the line of the keel.

Side lanterns should be fitted on the bridge-ends whenever
possible.

12. *Lanterns in the Rigging*—Small sailing ships which
cannot with safety and convenience of working, carry their
side lanterns on stanchions, may carry them in the rigging
provided the Surveyor is satisfied that they are so fitted that
their light is visible for the distance and in the direction
required by the Collision Regulations and will not be obscured
by the sails.

Sound Signals

13. *Bells*—All power-driven vessels and sailing vessels of
12 metres or more in length must be provided with an efficient
bell. The bell should be hung in the forepart of the vessel,
clear of all obstructions and should be not less than 300 mm.
in diameter at the mouth, except in the case of small vessels
under 50 metres in length, when a bell of not less than
200 mm. in diameter may be accepted.

K*

14. *Whistles*—All power-driven vessels are required to be provided with an efficient whistle sounded by steam or some substitute for steam, and so placed that the sound may not be intercepted by any obstruction. The whistle should be at least 3 m. above the deck, forward of the foremost funnel and well clear of, and above, deckhouses, ventilators, etc.

A whistle is not normally to be regarded as efficient unless it is audible for at least two miles in a still condition of the atmosphere. On vessels of under 50 metres in length making coasting or short sea voyages, if a Surveyor is satisfied that it is impracticable to fit a whistle meeting this condition, any efficient whistle capable of producing the sound signals required by the Collision Regulations may be accepted provided that it is so placed that the sound from it is not unduly obstructed and will carry a distance of at least one mile. On small power-driven boats plying on rivers, on inland waters, or at sea not more than three miles from the coast, a whistle audible for half a mile may be allowed if it is impracticable to fit a whistle with a range of one mile.

Ordinary 'organ' whistles should, except on vessels under 50 metres in length, be not less than 750 mm. high and 125 mm. in diameter; 'harmony' whistles, 'bell chime' steam whistles, and steam whistles of any other type should be of proportionate dimensions; whistle pipes should not be less than 50 mm. outside diameter.

Steam pipes should be so arranged that a full supply of steam free from water of condensation will at all times be immediately available when the vessel is underway; it should not therefore be possible for water to lodge in the pipes. All steam pipes should be lagged.

Compressed air whistle may be accepted on all power-driven vessels provided that they have the ranges of audibility given above and that the standard of their construction is in all respects satisfactory.

Electric whistles may be accepted as auxiliary whistles, provided that they have the required ranges of audibility. Electric whistles may also be accepted for use as main whistles on small vessels on which neither steam nor compressed air is available. Details of electric whistles which have been accepted for these purposes are circulated to Surveyors.

15. *Fog Horns*—All power-driven vessels and sailing vessels of 40 feet or more in length are to be provided with an efficient fog horn, to be sounded by mechanical means.

Fog horns of the 'rotary' and 'crank bellows' type are the most efficient at present in use. 'Plunger' type fog horns are rarely found to be efficient, and should only be accepted if *entirely* satisfactory.

Horns blown by mouth cannot be accepted as efficient on vessels plying on the high seas, or in waters connected therewith navigable by sea-going vessels.

16. *Gongs*—All vessels of more than 100 m. in length must be provided, in addition to the bell, with a gong or other instrument the tone and sounding of which cannot be confused with that of the bell. The most suitable instrument has been found to be a 16 S.W.G. mild steel gong not less than 16 inches in diameter with a lip of 2 inches, but any other instrument which clearly meets the requirements of the Rule may be accepted. Precautions against corrosion should be taken, but the gong should not be painted. Vessels built after 1st January, 1976 must comply with the positioning and technical details of lights, shapes and sound-signalling appliances given in Annexes I and III of the International Regulations. *See* Rule 38 for exemptions.

GENERAL NOTICES

All Candidates for Certificates of Competency are required to be conversant with the general information, e.g. Notices regarding distress signals, life-saving, various special signals, etc., contained in the Dept. of Trade and Civil Aviation Book of Merchant Shipping Notices of interest to Shipmasters, Seamen and others concerned with Foreign-going and Home Trade Merchant Ships and Fishing vessels.

Part I contains notices of a permanent character and is revised and republished only once in every three to five years.

Part II, when next reprinted, will contain information respecting 'Distress and Rescue at Sea—Ships and Aircraft'.

In addition, for Foreign-going Vessels, the following Notices to Mariners are issued by the Admiralty:—(a) Daily Notices, (b) Weekly (complete) Edition of Notices, (c) Quarterly Edition. For Home Trade and Fishing Vessels, the following Notices to Mariners are issued:—(a) Daily Notices, (b) Weekly (Home Trade) Edition of Notices.

As the information given in these Notices is liable to be altered or cancelled, or new information given, Candidates are strongly advised to procure the latest issues, which should be carefully studied, prior to presenting themsleves for Examination.

The Notices to Mariners may be obtained from any Mercantile Marine Office in the United Kingdom, free of charge.

The following is important information culled from the latest Notices to Mariners:—

LIFE-SAVING ORGANISATION ON COAST OF THE UNITED KINGDOM

Information and Instructions for the Guidance of Masters and Seamen

In the event of your ship being in distress off, or stranded on, the coast of the United Kingdom, the following signals shall be used by life-saving stations when communicating with your ship, and by your ship when communicating with life-saving stations.

(*a*) **Replies from life-saving stations or maritime rescue units to distress signals made by a ship or person:—**

Signals	*Signification*
By day—Orange smoke signal or combined light and sound signal (thunderlight) consisting of three single signals which are fired at intervals of approximately one *By night*—White star rocket consisting of three single signals which are fired at intervals of approximately one minute.	'You are seen—assistance will be given as soon as possible.' (Repetition of such signals shall have the same meaning.)

If necessary the day signals may be given at night or the night signals by day

(*b*) **Landing signals for the guidance of small boats with crews or persons in distress:—**

Signals	*Signification*
By day—Vertical motion of a white flag or the arms or firing of a green star-signal or signalling the code letter 'K' (▬ ▪ ▬) given by light or sound-signalling apparatus. *By night*—Vertical motion of a white light or flare or firing of a green star-signal or signalling the code letter 'K' ▬ ▪ ▬) given by light or sound-signalling apparatus. A range (indication of direction) may be given by placing a steady white light or flare at a lower level and in line with the observer.	'This is the best place to land.'

Signals	*Signification*
By day—Horizontal motion of a white flag or arms extended horizontally or firing of a red star-signal or signalling the code letter 'S' (▪ ▪ ▪) given by light or sound-signal apparatus. *By night*—Horizontal motion of a white light or flare or firing of a red star-signal or signalling the code letter 'S' (▪ ▪ ▪) given by light or sound-signal apparatus.	'Landing here is highly dangerous.'

By day—Horizontal motion of a white flag, followed by the placing of the white flag in the ground and the carrying of another white flag in the direction to be indicated or firing of a red star-signal vertically and a white star-signal in the direction towards the better landing place or signalling the code letter 'S' (• • •) followed by the code letter 'R' (• — •) if a better landing place for the craft in distress is located more to the right in the direction of approach or signalling the code letter 'L' (• — • •) if a better landing place for the craft in distress is located more to the left in the direction of approach.

'Landing here is highly dangerous. A more favourable location for landing is in, the direction indicated.'

By night—Horizontal motion of a white light or flare, followed by the placing of the white light or flare on the ground and the carrying of another white light or flare in the direction to be indicated or firing of a red star-signal vertically and a white star-signal in the direction towards the better landing place or signalling the code letter 'S' (• • •) followed by code letter 'R' (• — •) if a better landing place for the craft in distress is located more to the right in the direction

Signals	*Signification*
of approach or signalling the code letter 'L' (■ ━ ■ ■) of a better landing place for the craft in distress is located more to the left in the direction of approach.	'Landing here is highly dangerous. A more favourable location for landing is in the direction indicated.'

(*c*) **Signals to be employed in connection with the use of shore life-saving apparatus:—**

Signals	*Signification*
By day—Vertical motion of a white flag or the arms or firing of a green star signal. *By night*—Vertical motion of a white light or flare or firing of a green star-signal.	In general—'Affirmative.' Specifically—'Rocket line is held.' 'Tail block is made fast.' 'Hawser is made fast.' 'Man is in the breeches buoy.' 'Haul away.'
By day—Horizontal motion of a white flag or arms extended horizontally or firing of a red star-signal. *By night*—Horizontal motion of a white light or flare or firing of a red star-signal.	In general—'Negative.' Specifically—'Slack away' 'Avast hauling.'

(*d*) **Signals to be used to warn a ship which is standing into danger:—**

Signals	*Signification*
The International Code Signals U or J.D. The letter U (·· —) flashed by lamp or made by foghorn, or whistle, etc.	'You are running into danger.'

If it should prove necessary, the attention of the vessel is called to these signals by a white flare, a rocket showing white stars on bursting, or an explosive sound signal.

ROCKET LIFE-SAVING APPARATUS

Should lives be in danger and your vessel be in a position where rescue by the Rocket Life-Saving Apparatus is possible, a rocket with line attached will be fired across your vessel. Get hold of this line as soon as you can. When you have got hold of it, signal to the shore as indicated in (c) 1 above.

Alternately, should your vessel carry a Line-Throwing Appliance and this is first used to fire a line ashore, which line would not be of sufficient strength to haul out the Whip, those on shore will secure it to a stouter line and when this is done will signal as indicated in (c) 1 above. On seeing this signal, haul in on the line until the stouter line is on board. Then make the signal as indicated in (c) 1 above, then proceed as follows:—

When you see the signal as indicated in (c) 1 made from the shore, haul upon the rocket line until you get a tail block with an endless fall rove through it (called the 'Whip').

Make the tail block fast, close up to a convenient position, bearing in mind that the fall should be kept clear from chafing on any part of the vessel, and that space must be left above the block for the hawser. Unbend the rocket line from the Whip. When the tail block is made fast and the rocket line unbent from the Whip, signal to the shore again as indicated in (c) 1 above.

As soon as this signal is seen on shore a hawser will be bent to the Whip, and will be hauled off to the ship by those on shore. Except when there are rocks, piles or other obstructions between the ship and the shore, a bowline will have been made with the end of the hawser round the hauling part of the Whip.

When the hawser is got on board, the bowline should be cast off. Then, having seen that the end of the hawser is clear of the Whip, the end should be brought up between the two parts of the Whip and made fast to the same part of the ship as the tail block BUT JUST ABOVE IT AND WITH THE TALLY BOARD CLOSE UP TO THE POSITION TO WHICH THE END OF THE HAWSER IS SECURED (this will allow the breeches buoy to come right out and will facilitate entry to the buoy).

When the hawser has been made fast on board, unbend the Whip from the hawser and see that the bight of the Whip has not been hitched to any part of the vessel and that it runs free in the block. Then signal to the shore as indicated in (c) 1 above.

The men on shore will then set the hawser taut, and by means of the Whip will haul off to the ship the Breeches Buoy into which the person to be hauled is to get. He should sit well down in the Breeches Buoy and when he is secure, signal again to the shore as indicated in (c) 1 above, and the men on shore will haul the person in the Breeches Buoy to the shore. When he is landed the empty Breeches Buoy will be hauled back to the ship. This operation will be repeated until all persons are landed.

It may sometimes happen that the state of the weather and

the condition of the ship will not admit of a hawser being set up: in such cases a Breeches Buoy will be hauled off by the Whip which will be used without the hawser.

The system of signalling must be strictly followed. It should however, be noted that while the signals referred to in (c) 1 above are made only when the crew have got hold of the rocket line; when the tail block has been made fast; when the hawser has been made fast; and when a person is in the Breeches Buoy ready to be hauled ashore, the rescue operation as a whole will be greatly facilitated if signal communication (by semaphore or flashing lamp) is established between the ship and the shore (or lifeboat). The large majority of life-saving Apparatus Companies and Lifeboats have trained signalmen.

All women, children, passengers, and helpless persons, should be landed before the crew of the ship. Masters and crews of stranded vessels should bear in mind that success in landing them by the Rocket Life-Saving Apparatus depends, in a great measure, upon their own coolness and attention to the instructions laid down.

During the course of the operations should it be necessary to signal, either from your ship to the shore, or from the shore to your ship, to 'Slackaway' or 'Avast hauling', this should be done as indicated in (c) 2 above.

CAUTION WITH REGARD TO SHIPS APPROACHING SQUADRONS, CONVOYS, AIRCRAFT CARRIERS AND OTHER WARSHIPS AT SEA AND AIRCRAFT CARRIERS AT ANCHOR

Squadrons and Convoys

(1) The attention of shipowners and mariners is called to the danger to all concerned which is caused by single vessels

approaching a squadron of warships, or merchant vessels in convoy, so closely as to involve risk of collision, attempting to pass ahead of, or through such a squadron or convoy . . .

(2) Mariners are therefore warned that single vessels should adopt early measures to keep out of the way of a squadron or convoy.

(3) The fact that it is the duty of a single vessel to keep out of the way of a squadron or convoy does not entitle vessels sailing in company to proceed without regard to the movements of the single vessel. Vessels sailing in a squadron or convoy should accordingly keep a careful watch on the movements of any single vessel approaching the squadron or convoy and should be ready, in case the single vessel does not keep out of the way, to take such action as will best aid to avert collision.

Aircraft Carriers

(4) Attention is also drawn to the uncertainty of the movements of aircraft carriers, which must usually turn into the wind when aircraft are taking off or landing.

(5) Furthermore, Mariners are warned that by night aircraft carriers have:—

    (*a*) Their steaming lights placed permanently off the centre line of the ship and at considerably reduced horizontal separation.

    (*b*) Alternative positions for their sidelights:—

      (i) On either side of the hull;

      (ii) On either side of the island structure, in which case the port bow light may be as much as 35 metres from the port side of the ship.

(6) Certain aircraft carriers exhibit anchor lights as follows:—

Four *white* lights located in the following manner:—

In the forward part of a vessel at a distance of not more than 1·5 metres below the flight deck, two lights in the same horizontal plane, one on the port side and one on the starboard side.

In the after part of the vessel at a height of not less than 5 metres lower than the forward lights, two lights in the same horizontal plane, one on the port side and one on the starboard side.

Each light visible over an arc of at least 180°. The forward lights visible over a minimum arc from one point on the opposite bow to one point from right astern on their own side, and the after lights from one point on the opposite quarter to one point from right ahead on their own side.

Replenishment-at-Sea

(7) British and Allied Warships in conjunction with auxiliaries frequently exercise Replenishment-at-Sea. While doing so the two or more ships taking part are connected by jackstays and hoses. They display the three lights in a vertical line: Red, White, Red, prescribed by Rule 27 (*b*) of the International Regulations for Preventing Collisions at Sea, 1972.

(8) Mariners are warned that while carrying out these exercises the ships are severely restricted both in manoeuvrability and speed and it is the duty of other vessels to keep well clear in accordance with Rule 2 of the above Regulations.

Certain Warships—Positions of Steaming Lights

(9) Certain other warships which, in accordance with Rule 23 of the International Regulations for Preventing

Collisions at Sea, cannot comply fully with the requirements as to the number and positioning of lights, comply as closely as possible.

The following vessels of 50 metres in length, or over, cannot be fitted with a second steaming light owing to their special construction:—Destroyers (including 'Daring' class), frigates, ocean and coastal minesweepers and boom working vessels.

(10) In addition, certain cruisers which cannot comply fully as regards the position of the second steaming light have a slightly reduced vertical separation between the two lights.

INFORMATION CONCERNING SUBMARINES
PART I—WARNING SIGNALS
(a) Visual Signals

1. Mariners are warned that considerable hazard to life may result by the disregard of the following warning signals, which denote the presence of Submarines:—

British vessels fly the International Code Group NE2 to denote that Submarines, which may be submerged, are in the vicinity. Vessels are cautioned to steer so as to give a wide berth to any vessel flying either of these signals. If from any cause it is necessary to approach her, vessels should approach at slow speed until warning is given of the danger zone by flags, semaphore or megaphone, etc., a good look-out being kept meanwhile for Submarines whose presence may be only indicated by their periscopes or snorts showing above water.

A Submarine submerged at a depth too great to show her periscope may sometimes indicate her position by releasing a 'smoke candle' which gives off a considerable volume of smoke on first reaching the surface. Her position may sometimes be indicated by red-and-white or red-and-yellow buffs or floats, which tow on the surface close astern.

(b) Pyrotechnics and Smoke Candles

2. The following signals are used by a submerged Submarine in a Submarine exercise area:—

Signal	Signification
One *red* pyrotechnic light, or smoke, repeated as often as possible.	Keep clear. I am carrying out emergency surfacing procedure. Do not stop propellers. Ships are to clear the area immediately and stand by to render assistance.
Two *yellow* pyrotechnic lights, or two *white* or *yellow* smokes, 3 minutes apart.	Keep clear. My position is as indicated. I intend to carry out surfacing procedure. Do not stop propellers. Ships are to clear the immediate vicinity.

It must not be inferred from the above that Submarines exercise only when in company with escorting vessels.

3. Under certain circumstances warnings that Submarines are exercising in specified areas may be broadcast by a General Post Office radio station.

PART II—NAVIGATION LIGHTS

4. Submarines may be met on the surface by night, particularly in the vicinity of the following ports:—

Thames Estuary, Portsmouth, Portland, Plymouth, Barrow, Liverpool, Londonderry and Clyde Areas.

5. Hitherto the navigation lights of submarines have been exhibited from the Conning Tower which is near the centre of the vessel. The steaming light, bow lights and overtaking light have been necessarily low down and closely spaced with the result that they give no indication of the submarine's length nor of her exact course or change of course. Consequently they may be mistaken for the lights of a very much smaller vessel of the coaster type.

6. Special arrangements have now been made to fit H.M. Submarines with a second steaming light. The forward steaming light is placed on a special fitting in the fore part of the vessel between 0·5 and 2 metres above the hull. The main steaming light is fitted on the conning tower or fin. In submarines where the forward steaming light is appreciably less than 2 metres above the hull, and may in consequence be lower than the coloured side lights, the overall arrangement of lights as seen from other vessels may appear unusual. In addition, the vertical separation in some cases is less than 4·5 metres.

The overtaking light is placed on a special fitting near the stern of the vessel but may be at a height considerably less than that of the side lights.

LIGHT VESSELS IN THE BRITISH ISLES

Regulations—The following Regulations have been established respecting the several light-vessels on the coasts of the British Isles, viz:—

A *white* riding light is exhibited from the forestay of each light-vessel, at a height of 2 metres above the rail, for the purpose of showing in which direction the vessel is riding when at her station.

If from any cause a light-vessel is unable to exhibit her usual *characteristic* lights whilst at her station, the riding light only will be shown.

The distinguishing masthead marks carried by light-vessels are painted *black*.

Light-vessel watch buoys are can buoys painted *red*, with 'Watch' proceeded by the light-vessel's name in *white* letters. (Watch buoys are not moored off Scottish or Irish Coast light-vessels, or in the area of Mersey Docks and Harbour Board, and Humber Conservancy Board.)

During fog or low visibility, on the near approach of any traffic to a light-vessel, the bell of the light-vessel will be rung rapidly during the silent intervals between each sounding of the vessel's prescribed station fog signal until all risk of collision is past.

When a light-vessel is driven from her proper station to one where she is of no use as a guide to shipping, the distinguishing masthead marks, where carried, will be struck, if circumstances permit. The characteristic light will not be shown and the fog signals will not be sounded but the following signals will be made:—

By day—2 large *black* balls will be shown, one forward and one aft, and the signal *LO*, indicating 'I am not in my correct position,' will be hoisted where it may best be seen.

By night—A *red* fixed light will be shown at each end of the vessel and *red* and *white* flares shown simultaneously *every* 15 *minutes* or at more frequent intervals on the near approach of traffic; flares to be shown, from where they can best be seen, at a distance of about 9 m. apart in a horizontal line. If the use of flares is impracticable, a *red* light and

a *white* light will be displayed simultaneously for
about a minute.

In fog or low visibility, light-vessels out of position will
give the fog signal required for a vessel at anchor.

It should be remembered that light-vessels, *through collision or other causes*, are liable to be withdrawn for
repairs, without notice, and in some cases may not
be replaced by relief vessels.

COLLISIONS WITH LIGHT VESSELS

Caution—Light vessels have been run into on several
occasions by vessels navigating in their vicinity, and the lives
of the men on board the light vessels have been seriously
endangered, the attention of mariners is drawn to the importance of making due allowance for the set of the tide and of
exercising every precaution in order to GIVE ALL LIGHT VESSELS
A WIDE BERTH, especially when crossing their bows in a tideway,
which should never be attempted unless absolutely necessary.

Under Section 666 of the Merchant Shipping Act, 1894, any
person wilfully or negligently running foul of any lightship or
buoy is liable, in addition to the expense of making good any
damage so occasioned, to a fine not exceeding £50 for each
offence.

VESSELS NAVIGATED STERN FOREMOST

It has been agreed with the owners of the British vessels
chiefly concerned that the following signal should be displayed
by vessels which are fitted with bow rudders and are navigated
stern foremost when entering or leaving certain ports and
harbours in the United Kingdom and abroad, to indicate that
for the time being they are navigating stern foremost:—

Two balls, each 0·6 metre in diameter, carried at the ends
of a horizontal jackyard on the mast or, if the vessel has more

than one mast, on the main or after-mast. The jackyard will be placed in a thwartship direction, at least 2 metres higher than the funnel top and will project at least 1·5 metre on either side of the mast, so that the distance between the centres of the two balls will be at least 3 m.

Bye-laws giving effect to this arrangement have been made for the ports of Dover, Ramsgate, Holyhead, Larne, Belfast, Clyde, Heysham, London, Fishguard, Folkestone and Harwich.

BUOYS AND BEACONS

Wrecks have occurred through undue reliance on buoys and floating beacons always being maintained in their exact position.

They should be regarded simply as aids to navigation and not as infallible marks, especially when placed in exposed positions.

The lights shown by gas buoys cannot be implicitly relied on as, if occulting, the apparatus may get out of order; or the light may be altogether extinguished.

A ship should always, when possible be navigated by bearings or angles of fixed objects on shore and not by buoys or floating beacons.

VISUAL AND SOUND SIGNALS

The experience of the Department of Trade shows that two of the existing statutory distress signals, viz.: 'a continuous sounding with any fog-signal apparatus' and 'flames on the vessel' are not only liable to abuse, but when used as distress signals have often given rise to misunderstanding. A succession of signals on the whistle or siren is frequently made for other purposes than of indicating distress, e.g. for summoning a pilot, and may be mistaken for a 'continuous sounding'. Similarly, working lights and 'flare up' lights are authorised for use by fishing vessels and other small craft, and the simplest way of making a 'flare up' light is to dip a rag in paraffin and set it alight. Unfortunately small vessels in distress frequently make the signal 'flames on the vessel' in the same manner. Thus it is often impossible to decide whether 'flare up' lights are being shown or whether distress signals are being made, especially in areas where fishing is carried on. As a result, uncertainty and delay have occurred and lives have been lost in consequence.

FOG SIGNALS

Sound is conveyed in a very capricious way through the atmosphere. Apart from wind, large areas of silence have been found in different directions and different distances from the signals, in some instances even when in close proximity to the sound signal.

The mariner should not assume:—

1. That he is out of ordinary hearing distance, because he fails to hear the sound.
2. That because he hears a fog signal faintly, that he is a great distance from it.
3. That he is near it, because he hears the sound plainly.
4. That the distance from and the intensity of the sound on any one occasion is a guide to him for any future occasion.
5. That the fog signal has ceased sounding, because he does not hear it even when in close proximity.

Distress signals should be as distinctive as possible, so that they may be recognised at once and assistance despatched without delay. Thus, instead of making an indefinite succession of blasts on the fog signalling apparatus when in distress, mariners should make the 'continuous sounding' by repeating the Morse signal SOS ▪ ▪ ▪ ━ ━ ━ ▪ ▪ ▪ on the whistle or fog horn. If this is done there can be no mistake as to the meaning of the signal. Similarly, by night, if signalling for help by means of a lamp or flashing light the same signal SOS should always be used.

As regards the 'flames on the vessel' signal, unless the flames making the signal are sufficiently large to attract immediate attention their chances of being recognised as a distress signal are very poor. The best distress signals are red parachute flares or rockets emitting red stars, and wherever possible a supply of such signals should be carried. Arrangements should be made to steady rockets to ensure their satisfactory flight when fired. Where it is not practicable to use the foregoing types of signals, lifeboat 5-star red signals, which can be held in the hand while being discharged should be provided.

LIFELINES AND LIFEBUOYS ON FISHING VESSELS

Cases of loss of life through falling overboard from fishing vessels frequently occur, some of which would be avoided if lifelines were in use. Skippers of fishing vessels, and all other persons concerned, should keep lifelines continuously rigged at sea. Trawl warps may be used as lifelines.

Safety rails should be rigged in possition before, or as, the vessel leaves the quayside.

Lifebuoys should be kept where they will be available at a moment's notice. If used promptly a lifebuoy will sometimes serve as a guide to the whereabouts of the man overboard; otherwise he may be lost sight of while the vessel is being brought round to reach him.

APPROACHING IN ORDER TO SPEAK

In several collisions between fishing vessels which have recently come under notice, it has been apparent that the collision has been due to the dangerous practice of one fishing vessel approaching close to another in order that the skippers may discuss the fishing by word of mouth. In a recent case the approaching vessel was carried by wind and sea on to the other vessel and sank her, four lives being lost.

The Department of Trade wish to impress upon those responsible for the navigation of fishing vessels the danger of approaching to speak. Skippers will bear in mind that Courts of Inquiry have power to cancel or suspend the certificate of any skipper or certificated hand found to be in fault.

Danger of collision occurring through a fishing vessel approaching to speak can be avoided by the use of one or other of the signalling systems for which means should be available on board, e.g. morse lamp or semaphore or wireless telephony.

Damage to Drift Nets

The attention of Masters and Skippers is drawn to the heavy costs sustained by drift net fishing vessels which have had their nets destroyed or damaged by other ships. A merchant ship crossing drift nets not only causes damage to the nets but runs the risk of the gear becoming entangled in her propeller.

All seamen directly responsible for the safe navigation of their ships should take early action to keep well clear of drift-net vessels which at night are indicated by the arrangement of lights required by Rule 26 (c) of the Collision Regulations.

An all round white working light is commonly carried in the forepart of a vessel when she is lying to her nets and it is from this direction that the nets may extend ahead and to windward for a distance of up to two miles.   It is emphasised therefore that particular care must be taken to keep clear of this area.

The attention of Masters is also drawn to the advice on fisheries given in the appropriate Pilot Book.

Flares or a searchlight beam in direction of danger threatening approaching vessel are displayed by fishermen when vessels are observed to be bearing down on their fleet of nets.

where to a distance of up to 1.25 miles. It is emphasised, therefore, that particular care must be taken to keep clear of this area.

The addition of 'Master' is an addition to the directions.

Caution given in the appropriate Pilot Book.

There are searchlight beacons in one area of danger. Sometimes optimum than vessel are swamped by the current, when vessels are cautioned to be beating down on their lives of risk.